SPIDER ZERO
SEVEN

MIKE BORLACE

Matador
9 Priory Business Park,
Wistow Road, Kibworth Beauchamp,
Leicestershire. LE8 0RX
Tel: 0116 279 2299
Email: books@troubador.co.uk
Web: www.troubador.co.uk/matador
Twitter: @matadorbooks

ISBN PB: 978 1788038 959
HB: 978 1788038 966

British Library Cataloguing in Publication Data.
A catalogue record for this book is available from the British Library.

Printed and bound by CPI Group (UK) Ltd, Croydon, CR0 4YY
Typeset in 11pt Minion Pro by Troubador Publishing Ltd, Leicester, UK

Matador is an imprint of Troubador Publishing Ltd

Spider Zero Seven

*This book is dedicated to the real heroes of the Rhodesian
Air Force:
All of the technician/gunners of 7 Squadron*

*But most especially to the memory of
"Hajj"
Flight Sergeant Henry Allan James Jarvie, MFC
Killed in action, Mtoko, 12 January 1978*

A special thank you to those that encouraged me to write this and to my family, Angela, Jon-Selous and Sally. Patrick King for providing the framework, Patrick Mavros for providing a prod when it was needed, Sophie Gillespie for editing, and the production people at Matador. George Ashton-Jones of the Compost Heap for the cover, Ian Lynn for the video.

Nor law, nor duty bade me fight,
Nor public men, nor cheering crowds,
A lonely impulse of delight
Drove to this tumult in the clouds

William Butler Yeats (1865–1939)

Contents

Prologue

We are flying really low, weaving slightly through the thorn and acacia bushes, the wheels brushing through the tops of the long grass. I have a last look at the folded map held between my right hand and the cyclic to get the mental picture organised in my mind, and then tuck the map away. I have a niggling doubt that we are in the wrong valley as the OP has reported that the terrorist group has not started to bombshell on hearing our approach, but the second hand of my watch is coming up to 11:47 and I reckon we are half a minute from their reported position.

"K-Car is thirty seconds out. Pulling up. All callsigns stay off this frequency, there is a punch-up in progress."

I raise the nose and start to convert speed into height; I want to be at five to six hundred feet above the target. The gunsight is calibrated for us to be at eight hundred and fifty feet, but I am a believer in the better you can see the target, the better you will shoot. I turn slightly right to offset us in order that the cannon can come straight into play firing to the left. The horizon expands rapidly as we climb.

"They're running! They're running!" excitedly from the OP.

I see them a couple of hundred yards ahead.

"Oh-kaay, we are in contact. G-Cars go in a wide orbit," on the radio. "Got them visual? Open fire when you're ready. Take the group together first," on the intercom.

Four of the group are running fast away from us westwards along the valley but the other four are standing together and firing at us. There is a lot of popping around the aircraft; their fire is close, but they're not hitting us yet. I roll the aircraft quite gently to the left and ease my view of the door catch on the central pillar of the cockpit onto the group of four. This acts as a rough gun sight the cannon is then in a comfortable position for the gunner. I see the barrel move slightly as the gunner peers through his sight and there is a crash, the smell of burning explosive and the whole helicopter judders as he lets off a three-or four-round burst. The rounds hit the ground about ten feet from the group but one of them crumples to the ground; they are HEI – high-explosive incendiary – twenty-millimetre calibre, and explode into hundreds of red hot pieces of shrapnel when they hit. As the others start to move apart, the gunner makes a quick adjustment and slams down three quick bursts right into the middle of the group. They all fall to the ground.

"Put down some more." I don't want this lot snivelling away whilst we deal with the others, and he puts three more bursts down into the four prone bodies.

We are not even halfway around the first orbit, so instead of continuing in our left turn I roll the aircraft violently to the right and back to the left when the nose is positioned to take on the next target, a lone gook high-stepping it through the scrub, and getting too close to dense bush into which he is likely to disappear. He falls after four bursts; he is running so fast it takes a moment to gauge the lay-off. I get the gunner to put down another burst to make sure he stays down and position us for the sixth. He has taken cover by an anthill, good cover against ground troops but it is not going to help him from us. It looks as though he is carrying an RPD machine gun but he is not firing it and appears to be trying to hide in the scrub. It probably looks quite thick from his point of view, but we can see him easily and the gunner hits him on the first burst. I have been watching three of the G-Cars about a quarter of a mile away out of the corner of my eye. They are in a fairly tight low-level orbit and three streams of tracer are hosing out towards another anthill.

"OK, Yellow, move out, we're on the target."

The trooper aircraft ceases firing and extends its orbit as we come overhead, locate the guy trying to burrow out of sight in the thorn bush around the anthill, and despatch him with three more bursts. There is no sign of the eighth member of the group, and we widen our orbit to search for him. The last one was already more than a kilometre from the initial contact position, which demonstrates how fast you can cover ground when there is a deadly incentive to encourage you.

"K-Car, this is two seven Bravo," this is the relay station on the big brick near Buhera. "Do you have a sitrep for ComOps?"

"Two seven Bravo. Tell them we are in contact and the score at this time is seven out of eight."

I see some birds explode into flight out of a tree, and as I look I notice further movement, and then blue denim amongst the branches. The bugger has climbed into a tree. That's fairly unusual. I direct the gunner to the tree and although he doesn't see the gook himself a sustained burst sends branches and debris into the air and a body falls into a heap at the foot.

"Two seven Bravo, make that eight out of eight. We are clearing up here and will be refuelling at Gwanda."

I look at my watch. It is 11:51. In four explosively violent minutes, eight men have died. It has been the one hundred and forty-ninth time I have led a fire force into a successful contact inside Rhodesia, is one of the fastest ten out of ten punch-ups on record, and as it turns out it is the last time I will do it. Three days later I leave Shabani for Salisbury and start the process of leaving the squadron.

The Author

Mike Borlace, combat pilot and special forces soldier, first achieved military distinction in Rhodesia (now Zimbabwe) during the 1970s.

Born in Cornwall, England, Mike was trained in the Royal Air Force and Royal Navy, becoming an operational commando helicopter pilot.

In 1974, he was recruited into the Rhodesian Air Force, ostensibly to fly Hawker Hunters, but his helicopter experience took him onto 7 Squadron, at that time becoming heavily engaged in the terrorist war and stretched for trained personnel.

Of the 1,096 days he served in 7 (Helicopter) Squadron, 793 days were on combat operations. During this period 327 days were as a gunship pilot and fireforce commander, resulting in 149 contacts with the enemy, in addition to 204 fireforce operations that resulted in no contact. He undertook eighty-two casevacs and ninety-nine operations with the Rhodesian SAS, the Selous Scouts and Rhodesian Light Infantry Commandos on cross-border raids, including several hot extractions of compromised troops under fire. He was shot down five times and wounded twice, and is one of only five holders of the Silver Cross, the highest gallantry award given to members of the Rhodesian Air Force.

Mike's service record could easily be mistaken for a movie script except that real life is often more extraordinary than the wildest fiction. In 1978, he left the air force to join the highly secret Selous Scouts, a special forces unit responsible for sixty-eight percent of all the kills by the Rhodesian security forces.

In the wake of the atrocity of a civilian airliner being shot down and some of the survivors being raped and bayoneted to death, he volunteered to operate as an undercover agent in the city of Lusaka, Zambia, gathering information on terrorist installations and defences, and specifically the location of the terrorist leader Joshua Nkomo. A plan was hatched to assassinate Nkomo; however, Mike was captured after being betrayed by a traitor in Rhodesian intelligence.

He was interrogated under torture, taken for mock execution three times and kept naked and chained in a six foot by eight foot cage for over six months in solitary confinement. In 1980, the warring factions agreed to a ceasefire agreement but the Zambian authorities reneged on a deal to repatriate him and instead he was charged on various counts of espionage and put on trial for his life. The High Court of Zambia was horrified at the accounts of torture and released him, only for the government to immediately rearrest him. Weeks later, after much secret brokering, he was quietly spirited out of custody and deported to London.

In 1982, he began a new career as a private military advisor for Western-backed allies around the globe, including operations in Sri Lanka against the Tamil Tigers and fighting the Revolutionary United Front in Sierra Leone, who were gratuitously maiming children throughout the land by chopping off their arms and eating them. In 1986, he was running a team for the Americans flying into Nicaragua, supplying arms to the anti-communist Contra organisation. It was a mission controlled by Lieutenant-Colonel Oliver North and one that, after he had pulled his team out, ultimately led to the "Irangate" scandal.

Other deployments have been in Papua New Guinea, Angola, Uganda, South Sudan, and on contract with US agencies in Zaire, Afghanistan and Iraq.

I have known and shared adventures with Mike for over thirty-five years, so it was a real pleasure to be asked to help produce his book and a documentary about the Rhodesian conflict. Apart from his battlefield courage, he has the ability to assess dangerous situations quickly. That intelligence, together with his bravery, sense of humour and personality, come to life in the pages of *Spider Zero Seven*.

Patrick King, Producer,
Westminster King Productions, 2017

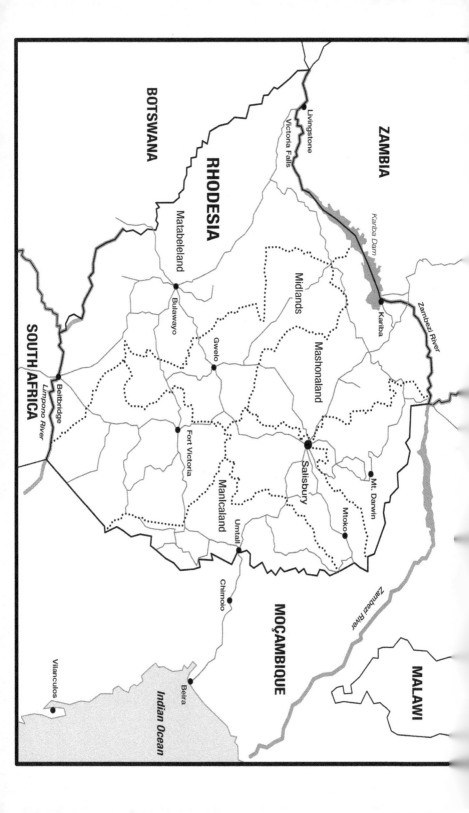

Introduction

The various squadrons of the Rhodesian Air Force were allocated individual code names – 'Panzer' for the 1 Squadron Hunters, 'Hornet' for 4 Squadron, 'Eagle' for 5 Squadron's Canberras, 'Dolphin' for the Dakotas – with specialised command post aircraft known as 'Warthog'. The helicopter squadron was designated 'Spider', with those of 8 Squadron, when it was formed, 'Cheetah'. Within every squadron each pilot had an individual call sign, the squadron commander being Zero One. Hence, within 7 Squadron, my call sign was "Spider Zero Seven".

I apologise for the liberal use of the pronoun "I" throughout this book. It is not an autobiography nor does it claim to be a definitive history of those times. It is a story. An attempt to convey some of the complex feelings, atmosphere and relationships of being involved in those years that those not on 7 Squadron were both lucky enough to avoid and unlucky enough not to have experienced and survived. I think all of us that did so would not change the experience – but the memory is very selective in editing out the tensions, terrors and frustrations and concentrating on the relief and humour. That is a good thing.

This story is the way I saw it, or at least the way I remember it. So any mistakes are mine entirely. I know there are no deliberate misrepresentations, but I am sure there will be errors of detail, but they are unimportant. If you do notice any clangers or too liberal use of poetic license, before you start wailing and throwing your toys out of the cot I would ask you to pause and remember the words of Huckleberry Finn – '*There was things which he stretched, but mainly he told the truth*'. Even eyewitnesses see things in a different way; Schulie and I, who were the principal eyewitnesses at Madula Pan, argue to this day about the actual sequence of events. Also, if you can really identify a major error of detail it means you are a member of a very exclusive club – you were there. And there weren't too many of us around at whatever moment of time and particular place that was.

If anybody is truly offended by any remark herein, and can convince me their recollection is more accurate, I will apologise publicly and post a video drinking an aabf flaming Drambuie and eating the glass on ORAFs, which is a frightening enough sight to belay most complaints. If you don't know what an aabf is, you certainly weren't there.

CHAPTER ONE

Early Days

I open one of the anonymous large brown envelopes and am surprised to read, "Thank you for your enquiry and interest in joining the Rhodesian Air Force.

What is this? I am, in fact, just about to accept a position as a contract officer flying Hunters for the air force of the Sultan of Oman and, as it happens, one of the other anonymous brown envelopes contains the final paperwork for that contract.

I am a little mystified by the letter until I recall being in the Red Lion off South Audley Street during my previous trip to London. It is an old – principally ex-naval – aircrew watering hole, and I am there with a couple of friends swapping flying lies. One of our group is an old Fleet Air Arm legend called Pete Sheppard, of a previous generation – he is an ex Sea Fury pilot. One of the other characters, the vintage and friend of Pete's, I remember had an ex Royal Air Force background, flying Meteors and Hunters. At one point he and I have a pretty detailed discussion about what my experience is and what I am planning to do. I find out later that it was 'Jock' (what a surprise) MacGregor, then serving in the Rhodesian Air Force, and trawling for experienced 'volunteers'.

I have heard good things about 'Southern' Rhodesia; a lot of the older flying instructors still serving had trained there during World War II, and all speak well of it. The country itself has been in and out of the news since UDI although I haven't heard too much in recent times. Friends of mine in the Navy were on HMS Tiger and HMS Fearless when talks were held between Harold Wilson and Ian Smith, and all remarked on the latter's courtesy and manners as opposed to the attitude of the former, who may well have been one of the highest placed assets the Soviets ever had in the UK.

Initially dismissive, I make some enquiries and then postpone the Oman decision and exchange a series of letters with the Rhodesians – they implore me to be discreet and keep things close to my chest. There is an astonishing amount of administrative detail to go through, including getting a full and certified service aircrew medical rating without divulging who it is for. Luckily, I have a really good contact in that line – Ruth, who is not a doctor but a medical specialist at St Mary's, calls in a favour from a fellow antipodean, who is a doctor. We have a problem with the section certifying that I am free of schitsamotosis; he has never heard of it, and it is no good asking me, my medical knowledge is such that I think paediatrics is something to do with your feet. He signs to say I am clear anyway, and we discover after the form has been sent back that it relates to bilharzia.

Eventually I get an offer to come and play with them. I have a few beers on a grey, drizzly London afternoon in Covent Garden. By chance I get into conversation with a nearby group. One of the girls is not long over from Rhodesia, and is the manager of an adjacent wine bar, to which we move. I wake up in a flat in Dolphin Square, admire the sleeping form beside me and reflect that the Oman thing is essentially like being at sea – i.e. no people with bumps on their chest – for nine months of the year. I call Airworks and say I won't be available for at least a year – no sense in burning your bridges – and send the letter back to Salisbury, via the South African Embassy – saying yes please.

There is a bit of toing and froing over the next fortnight with an embedded cell of Rhodesians in the South African embassy

– entering and leaving you run the gauntlet of the permanent anti-apartheid detachment camped outside in Trafalgar Square, and I presume everybody is also photographed as they go through the door – one false start, and then I am given a voucher to exchange with South African Airways.

A final drinks session with some ex-naval mates in the Antelope and the Duke of Boots and I pick up my two holdalls and set sail for Heathrow and points south.

I see Salisbury for the first time approaching in an SAA Boeing late on a Friday afternoon. I am struck by my first sight of a beautiful sunlit city rising out of the surrounding bushveld – it is small enough, and the horizons so wide, that you can see the whole conglomeration.

I am met by an air force warrant officer with a greeting:

"We were expecting you two weeks ago."

There are some monosyllabic answers to my odd questions on the drive in to town – not much difference there than to warrant officers in Britain – he's obviously late for prayers in the Sergeants' Mess. He deposits me at the Oasis Motel, says he has no further instructions for me, and I have no further contact for three days. Well, it is a weekend, and they do model themselves on the Royal Air Force!

Two other direct entry pilots arrive, Chris Abrams from the Royal Air Force, and Bill McQuade, a two-tour ex Vietnam veteran lurking behind a huge walrus moustache.

Eventually, on Monday, Jock MacGregor materialises; we have breakfast at an outside café and he walks us into Air Force Headquarters in Causeway, makes the necessary introductions and leaves us to go through a normal administrative induction system that involves reams of paper providing answers to the same questions again and again. It finally finishes with an interview with the deputy commander, Frank Mussel, the main theme of which is that we mustn't expect ever to become the commander, even if we turn our three year contracts into medium-term commissions. He obviously hasn't fully appreciated all of our previous backgrounds.

We are sworn in a bit later and then I am called into the presence of one of the heavies. He has my file on his desk and makes sure it is signed and locked away before delivering the time-honoured ritual that military people have had since time immemorial – for heaven's sake, it was the Royal Navy that invented the press gang. It has always been assumed that I will go to the Vampire and/or Hunter squadrons; I probably have more time than most of the Rhodesian pilots on DF/GA, but they have noticed my time on a naval commando assault helicopter squadron, and I will go, for a while at least, to the helicopter squadron.

I am not that bothered, maybe a little surprised; my initial enquiries have already ascertained that Thornhill, the jet base in the centre of the country, is not the social centre of the world, and initial recces have confirmed that in general, the Salisbury girls are as fit, tanned and as energetic as the bar manager in London, and are quite often in town on their own from the outlying farms. The climate is amazingly equable, and Lord Byron seems to have had a great influence in the girls' schooling –'*What men call gallantry, and the gods adultery, is much more common where the climate's sultry*'. The helicopters are based here in Salisbury.

William Logan (Bill) McQuade and I are introduced to 7 Squadron and join a course with three other pilots, none of whom have flown helicopters before. This is a pleasant enough interlude but at times very frustrating. The aerodynamics manual the Rhodesian Air Force are working from is way out of date, and the current theories on how helicopters stay in the air have superseded it, but the Rhodesians are not even interested in hearing any discussion.

We do exactly the same syllabus as the three others on the course, rather than evolving a far more efficient way of using the time, doing a conversion onto the two types of Alouette and then spending the hours familiarising ourselves with map-reading in the unfamiliar terrain, and acquainting ourselves with the operational techniques the squadron uses. One would have thought that an air force that had been estranged from the normal interchange of ideas with other services by the imposition of sanctions would hoover in any information they could from foreign volunteers – whether or not they subsequently tried to adopt those ideas. However, the Rhodesians, and the air force in particular, seemed both to be xenophobic and convinced that only they had the definitive answers to flying, and it was an attitude that prevailed right up to the time they handed themselves over to the enemy in 1980.

About eighteen months after I went through the heli course, when, rather like moving into an English village, I had become an accepted member of the community, I was called in by the squadron commander and chief instructor and asked to pass comment on a new foreign recruit that they were considering scrubbing from the course. I couldn't believe what I was hearing; they were talking about Terrance Murphy, who had previously served as a major in the Royal Marines and been a Royal Navy trained QHI. He was just having the same minor problems as anybody else in coming to an unfamiliar aircraft and learning its foibles – the Alouette was the first helicopter that most British and American pilots had met where the main blades rotate in the opposite direction (the Russians and French for some reason designing them that way) which causes changes to inbred automatic control inputs. Terrance had both flying and military experience that outweighed the vast majority of anybody in the security forces. He was to become one of the best fireforce leaders of the war, once let out on operations.

At the end of our course we were asked to write a critique, and I didn't exactly enamour myself to my new colleagues by commenting that I thought the 'academic flying' was the best I had ever seen – I can remember being stunned at the accuracy of the instrument flying of Kevin Peinke, who was at that time a relatively junior pilot, when acting as the safety pilot on a mutual flight – but that their operational techniques could be vastly improved. Individually, most of the operational pilots were aggressive and innovative, but the staff doctrine was years behind the drag curve. I don't believe the air force as an institution ever hoisted on board that they were fighting a war to the death, and were largely waiting for the day when sanctions were lifted and they could buy some shiny jets and resume running what they envisaged as a proper air force. Few of the staff had operational experience in a hostile COIN environment, and particularly with regard to the employment of helicopters.

Bill McQuade has additional problems. He has two tribal ones – being American, and coming from a military background that leads to confrontations about saluting, the use of forenames and the like. There is an episode when he and I have to take a technical exam in a hurry for some administrative reason. It is basically a 'rubber stamp' exercise, and Ted Lunt, who is invigilating, gives us a nod towards pages 57 to 60 of the manual that is on the table next to us and leaves us to answer the question on the paper.

Bill manages to copy out the wrong pages, and then refuses to retake the exam as "it's a crock of shit anyway – they stopped thinking like that years ago". The rubber stamp appears and the matter is quietly forgotten.

The course itself trundles along. To me, the Alouette 2 is a nightmare to fly as they have stripped out the hydraulics, and George Wrigley, the instructor, and I don't really gel. He has absolutely the most accurate flying technique of any helicopter pilot I have seen to date, so I am probably just jealous. On the Alouette 3 I fly with Rob McGregor – no relation to the head of the press gang – who is a pleasure to fly with, and the aircraft handles much better.

There are several enjoyable detachments, including a sort of aerial safari at Kariba for ten days, and the same in the mountains of Chimanimani, which provide for some spectacular flying in an area that most people have seen only from a distance. We take our handling check rides and the other three go back to Salisbury whilst Bill and I are given a familiarisation excursion along the north-eastern border – I think as a result of our suggestion that some of the course hours could have been better utilised.

There is an interesting incident during this trip. Throughout my time with the air force I am never impressed with the standard of lookout – in the latter days of the war two of the 1 Squadron fighter pilots are severely embarrassed when they are sent to escort the aircraft of a visiting envoy from the USA into Rhodesian airspace. On arriving at the designated rendezvous point, they are in the process of reporting that they are not visual with anybody, when a laconic drawl straight off the prairie tells them to look in their right two o' clock high; he has had them visual for the last minute. I suppose in the vast African sky with very few aircraft around, lookout isn't given the same priority as in the crowded skies of Europe. Anyway, George and I are flying along the Zambezi getting some great game viewing of crocs and hippo when he is surprised as I grab the cyclic and roll rapidly right as a low-wing pusscat Cessna or Piper passes close aboard going in the other direction. His anger dies quickly when he realises we have just missed a mid-air. When he calls the other aircraft on the common frequency it transpires that they didn't even see us as they were also game-viewing. The pilot is a tobacco farmer from Karoi, Jim Barker, whom George knows – at this early stage of my time in Rhodesia I hadn't yet appreciated that everybody knows, or at least knows of, everybody else. If they're not directly related, the families are probably related by marriage somewhere along the line – I come to realise that by their mid-twenties most of the girls are on their third marriage, so the whole country appears to be one great clan. Jim invites us to call in at his farm for lunch the next day.

This is the first time I have experienced this 'come by for lunch' concept, but the Rhodesians are genuinely the most hospitable race on earth, and it is a ritual that I enthusiastically embrace in the years to come. We land the next day on the manicured lawns of a magnificent farm and have a superb lunch eaten off bone china, cut-glass crystal and a highly polished stinkwood dining table. The farm is truly fabulous.

I am a little puzzled, however, that the interior rear wall of the sumptuous dining room has a couple of metal framed windows in it that look like a relic from the post-war prefabricated buildings of England. Jim's wife is obviously much younger than he, although her long hair has gone prematurely grey, and notices my puzzlement. She explains that when they came to the land in the late 1940s it was virgin bushveld. They lived initially in a tent, then a mud hut, and the prefab was their first actual house after a couple of years. When they finally started to make the farm pay and were able to afford to build the magnificent home they now had, they built it around the original shack, in order that they would never forget how hard they had had to work to wrest cultivation out of the bush.

George later fills me in with the rest of this extraordinary woman's story. In an early incursion of terrorists a few years previously, she had walked into the farm store to pick up her children off the school bus. Inside were three terrorists who had the children and storekeeper prisoner and informed her they were going to kill them all. She pleaded with them to kill her if they must but to let the children free. The terrorists were so impressed with her bravery in the face of their threats that they left without causing any of them injury. The young Judy Barker woke up the next morning and her hair had turned grey overnight.

Rob McGregor leads me out in two-ship formation to spend a week's supervised operations with a fireforce. We flog out to an encampment on the top of a bare rock kopje – Mutawatawa – from whence the fireforce is operating – and get settled in under canvas. The following morning there is a wailing siren at first light; the fireforce is being deployed to a contact in progress. Due to the nature of the ground, the aircraft are parked higgledy-piggledy and people are rushing in all directions. There is a hurried briefing which I don't really understand and Rob says to get airborne and follow him. I am still getting dressed; I can't get my leg into my trousers and there are buckets of rice pouring all over the rock as I struggle with the pants beside the door of my aircraft before discarding them and jumping aboard to the bemusement of the stick of troops in the back. On my last night in Salisbury I'd asked the girls in the 'Birdcage', a flat of five hospitable Air Rhodesia girls, to sew me a couple of 'see-through' pockets on my flying trousers. Apparently Rhodesian girls don't do casual sewing, and they ensure I have registered the lesson by sewing the legs closed, and filling all the pockets with rice. Won't make that mistake again.

From my point of view the contact is chaotic; I can hardly understand the cacophony of RT calls, and if Rob had not been there to shepherd me onto the LZ where the leader wanted my stick of troops, I would have had no idea of what he was talking about. However, by about the third callout it is all making a bit of sense, and at least I am turning up for battle fully dressed.

CHAPTER TWO

Mukumbura

I've had a couple of short bush tours on fireforce duties, living on top of the big brick at Mutawatawa which has enabled me to shake out operating as a G-Car driver, after the apparently chaotic cacophony of radio calls and aircraft manoeuvring of the first contact I was in. I had the good fortune of having Rob McGregor as the formation leader, who was able to nurture me through this baptism. Now my first long deployment is to FAF 4 – Mount Darwin – with Phil Tubbs as my crewman/gunner. Phil is one half of the Jarvie/Tubbs comedy act and plays straight man to Henry, who at this point I haven't met. Darwin is the focus of operations in the Op Hurricane area. A dedicated new airfield is under construction, and for the moment we are operating the helicopters from a pad near the JOC operations room. When a callout is initiated, we brief at the pad, lift off empty and pick the fireforce troops up off the nearby tar road, where they have formed up in sticks staggered along the road in order that they can embark the helicopters simultaneously. Then we make a rolling take-off and set sail to wherever the war is that day. This means we can lift off at maximum all-up weight and are carrying the most fuel possible, hence giving us a longer radius of action and/or loiter time at the scene.

We settle into the routine of fireforce operations, which at that moment is fairly relaxed, interspersed with routine tasks such as resupplying or changing relay station teams and the regular casevacs due to terrorist atrocities against local tribesmen or after landmine detonations. Generally, as each task comes up, there is a loose rolling roster of the G-Car pilots who are detailed off in turn. However, with a new boy in the area the excuse is made to gain local knowledge by detailing most of the tasks to me and Tubbs, which is an excellent way of getting familiar with the local landmarks and terrain, in order that one isn't continually having to map read.

Terrible mutilations, torture and murders are carried out by terrorist groups on any locals suspected in the slightest way of being a 'sell-out', the qualifications for which are wide-ranging and can be, for instance, as innocuous as dipping your cattle in a government-administered cattle dip. There is much denouncing of sell-outs to the terrorist groups and, of course, the local population use this as an opportunity to settle old scores. The police Special Branch ground coverage teams do have a network of paid informants, who often supply pretty good intelligence on forthcoming terrorist meetings, movements and camps. These informants also help initiate contacts, and a system of bounty payments for weapons recovered after a contact where the terrorists are killed or captured, with the amount varying according to the terrorist's rank, so some of them have acquired very healthy little nest eggs indeed.

Landmines are an everyday fact of life, and often whilst at breakfast we hear the first ones of the morning detonate, having been laid during the night. The Rhodesian security forces have counter landmine technology pretty much in hand, using water-filled tyres to dissipate energy, rubber conveyor belting to absorb shrapnel and blast, weighting of the vehicles with sandbags, and so on, and latterly designing or modifying vehicles with V-shaped chassis to deflect the blast. As a result, most SF casualties due to mines are now as a result of the subsequent road accident being due to the driver travelling too fast and losing control when the blast occurs, rather than from the mine itself. However, mines are not in any way discriminatory, and terrible casualties are inflicted on the locals when they are detonated by scotch carts, tractors and buses.

There is a mission hospital at Karanda run by an American doctor, Drake, who is the nearest to a saint I have ever met. He has in some earlier parts of his life been a US Navy pilot and then a successful neuro-surgeon in California. He runs the hospital, performing all required medical services for the local population, and refuses in any way to become involved with the political situation. It is known that he has treated wounded terrs that have been brought in to him as equally as he treats our own wounded soldiers, whom we often take there straight out of a contact for immediate treatment, in preference to the military facilities. Despite the known collaboration with the enemy, which technically carries the threat of the death penalty, a blind eye is turned as it is generally accepted that the man and the mission hospital are an oasis of stability, genuine compassion and good in the nastiness of the operational area. Sadly, later in the war the terrs attack and burn the hospital to the ground. I think the staff survived, but I am not sure if it was rebuilt.

One morning, me and a South African, Neil Liddell, are called to the ops room and briefed to go to the scene of a landmine detonation. A bus has been blown up and there are a number of casualties. We arrive at a scene of absolute carnage; the bus had been largely full of school children. There are already several dead and many others very seriously injured. We shut down the helicopters and all of us get involved in life saving first aid.

Theoretically, this should not have been done. Professional troops would cover a landmine with an ambush, particularly if they expect casevac helicopters to come and land. However, professional soldiers don't blow up civilian buses at random, and I don't recall the terrorists ever covering a landmine with a subsequent ambush. It is irrelevant, there is no other humane alternative – there are a handful of people trying to sort out the casualties, most of whom are children between the ages of four and nine. Because they are infants we are able to load about ten or twelve at a time and carry them to Karanda mission. I pick up one little girl of probably six, to carry her to the helicopter. She is in absolute shock and wraps her arms round my neck, hugging me in a death grip. When I get to the helicopter we can't get her to let go so I don't bother with strapping in and she sits on my lap for the flight, eventually being gently prised off by the nurses at the mission. On the next flight I carry in a boy who is probably not old enough to walk. The nurses say to take him straight into the operating room where Drake is operating simultaneously on three patients – whilst the assistant swabbed or stitched or whatever on one, he just carries on with one of the others for a minute or so and then comes back to the first. I am standing watching this with the kid in my arms when he stops breathing.

"Hey, doctor, this kid's stopped breathing." He looks up; I'm holding the child out.

"Grab that needle there and shove it into his chest by the heart."

"What?" I'm incredulous; I'm a pilot, holding a little child in a pair of filthy flying gloves, and he's telling me to put a bloody great needle in his chest.

"Do it! Quickly!" and then a little more gently, "Look, if he's already dead, you can't do any harm. Go on, do it!"

I put the syringe in gingerly, and depress the plunger. Amazingly, shortly afterwards he starts snuffling, snot comes down his nose and then he's whimpering; he's alive!

Neil and I get back some time after lunch, which we've missed. Having gone out before breakfast we're all hungry. Luckily, Darwin is joined to Salisbury by a tarmac road – no landmines – and some women's voluntary team runs a hotdog stall with a team of two doughnut dollies who come out for weekly stints, providing tea, buns and other odd home comforts for the boys in the bush.

The pilots all live in a corrugated wriggly tin building, which during the day is uninhabitable unless you fancy auditioning for a part as a Sunday roast. We all have our own cells in the building but the partitioning walls only go to the height of the outside walls, and are not continued up to the sloping roof, so as a result the slightest burp or fart is heard by everybody, almost before you'd realise you were going to do it yourself. Across the end of the hut is a slightly bigger room with three beds, for the use of any extra aircrew who may be stopping overnight.

I am just dropping off to sleep. There is a creaking as the door at the end of the building slowly opens.

"Are you sure nobody can hear us?" says a squeaky voice. I'm back from the world of Morpheus immediately. What's going on here?

"Naah, of course not," says a very slurred, drunken Neil Liddell. I'm absolutely wide awake now. Blimey, he's pulled one of the tea ladies.

It takes about thirty minutes of rustling, whispering, knicker snapping, her waking him up at least three times, and him falling off the bed once before they get their sports kit sorted out. Neil loses his way a couple of times, but she's determined to give him the full guided tour. By this stage, Neil's forgotten what he's there for, or at least the primary equipment has, but now she's really keen to make a go of it and after much tugging and cajoling, encouraging pep talks and a couple more wake up calls, he's eventually back on the blocks. Now it really starts. The bed jangles and creaks and groans, there's more gasping and louder pep talks, the odd lapse into temporary quiet, and a bit more waking up to do, before the whole tempo changes. The bed must be jumping up and down judging by the commotion, the whole building seems to be vibrating in resonance. There's so much wheezing and puffing going on it's like a steam train on a fast run. All of the wheezing seems to be from Liddell; she's moaning for Africa. It goes on and on and on. And on. He's obviously having the normal drunk's problem, but they finally move up another gear – I'm getting worried about the building falling in – and with much "Yes, yes, yessing" – not a lot of point in 'no' now – Neil finally tries his first words since assuring her they're in a soundproofed hideaway with the immortal line, "I'm coming. I'm coming."

It hasn't really occurred to me that it's not only me that is being treated to this, and there is a spontaneous cheer and much clapping and hooting from all the residents of the little tin shack. Suddenly there is absolute silence from the transit room, followed by a sotto voce.

"Neil. Neil," answered with an evocative, loud and long snore. After a few more whispered 'Neils' she realises she's on her own, ignores the odd call of "Come on, give him another one", and the sounds of dressing, opening doors and creeping away are a deal more furtive than the arrival.

Not exactly a blue movie, but the best entertainment for some time at Darwin. Liddell of course keeps the whole hut awake for about an hour with his snoring before somebody goes round and turns him on his nose or whatever you do.

The following day, business at the hot dog stand booms as the whole camp gets a liking for steak rolls and there is a permanent group of quietly ruminating aircrew trying to figure out which one it was. Liddell is questioned closely on the matter but claims he can't remember. He's probably telling the truth.

I'm told to report to the Scouts' fort for a briefing on a detachment to Mkumbura. There's much hilarity from the rest of the fireforce. It's not really my turn but because I'm the new boy apparently it'll be good for me to get down on the valley floor and find out what heat, dust and mopani flies really are. The briefing is by Neil Kriel, also known as the Kandeya Goat, a huge man covered in black hair; unkempt beard and moustache, shoulder-length hair, forearms the width of my thighs. A gorilla got into his family pedigree somewhere back in the past. He's been famously described by Gaps Newman as 'a walking armpit with eyeballs', and is the model for various cartoons featuring the Selous Scouts, with knuckles dragging along by his toes and a hand grenade in each paw.

The briefing is what it says, brief. I'm to proceed to Mkumbura, rendezvous with Captain Rob Warracker and he'll brief me on the task. No, I can't know how long I'll be away. Fine, what was the point of walking over to the fort and taking about ten minutes to gain entry, as the gate guards weren't expecting me and I didn't know the password? Nobody knows the password. Kriel questions me on my accent, background and how long I've been on the squadron. He's not happy about having a 'roineck' assigned to him. Having been told of the delights awaiting me on the valley floor, I try to edge him towards asking for a change, but he decides to make do with what he's got and off we go to pack our kit.

I return to our ops room and am taken to one side by the senior air force officer and have the rules spelled out to me about going over the border. Going over the border? This is the first time there's been any mention of it. Anyway, the rules are basically – don't. Only in the event of very serious casevac or the danger of death to a Rhodesian soldier am I allowed to cross, and preferably I should get authorisation from Air HQ beforehand.

Tubbs is moaning big time about his rotten luck being teamed with a gobby pilot. He's one of the old hands on the squadron, and could normally expect not to be saddled with the rougher tasks. We have a feed, and with Phil mumbling into his chops, and much ribaldry and a final, "Enjoy the Surf Club!" from my 'pals', we depart north, and after about half an hour get to the escarpment. I see the Zambezi Valley for the first time, the floor about a thousand feet below us, and about twenty clicks ahead, at the limit of visibility in the dust and heat haze, is a silver line, which is not the Zambezi but one of its tributaries, the Mkumbura river. I do a long cruise descent and get on the trees about halfway to Mukkers. You can feel the heat in the aircraft, and we're flying at ninety knots and have a bloody great fan operating over our heads. When we arrive at Mukkers and the rotors shut down, it's like stepping into an oven. Phil starts fussing around the aircraft. The bane of the technicians' lives is lubing the aircraft every five hours, along with the other standard checks, and the squadron engineering regime allows them to run a sort of flexible running schedule so that the aircraft are always ready to go. It is essential for bush operations in this environment, and the techs are very good and very conscientious about their duties. Even after all day fireforce punch-ups, when they've been fighting all day, the techs would always get whatever work was required on the aircraft out of the way before standing down.

I meet Warracker, we get accommodation sorted out, and he briefs me on the operation. A Scouts' patrol is crossing the border, marching for several days towards a known terrorist camp, which they will destroy before marching out. We are there for casevac/hot extraction duties, and to get airborne a couple of times a day to climb to a height where Rob can establish VHF comms with his team for a sitrep. This will save them from having to go through the lengthy rigmarole of setting up their HF radios. Well, all that seems simple enough, but they were right, this place is unbelievable. The heat is appalling, every time you slow down a cloud of mopani flies attaches itself to each and every orifice on your head, and the accommodation doesn't even have revolving fans. I may well sleep outside.

We're not allowed to cross the river on foot. What? Amazingly, people do. Openly, officially and quite legally. Mkumbura is an official border crossing point. Theoretically, we are still friends with the Mozambicans and the border is still open, although it is defined all along the Op Hurricane area with a fenced minefield on our side. However, the only people who go across are the customs officer and the local police for liaison purposes. The primary reason seems to be to return with Portuguese wine and beers.

Warracker and I get on OK. Initial sniffing around each other's tails and noses gives good karma both ways, and off we go to the famed Mkumbura Surf Club for sundowners. The Surf Club is the local SF bar, a sort of semi-bunker. They do their best with the wine and cervezas, but the generators have to be limited in their running time due to the logistics of getting fuel to this outpost of the empire, so the freezers never really get to grips with cooling the beers down, particularly at the rate they are consumed. I meet Tim Bax, who is the patrol leader, and after a while we strike a plan for us to use the helo to ferry them over the minefield some ways to the west of the town, rather than have the sappers breach the minefield for them to snivel over. It will turn a potential half-night exercise into about fifteen minutes at last light. Phil arrives and I tell him what we are going to do. He starts muttering about it being outside our remit, but isn't too serious about it, and then positively cheers up when Bax and Warracker buy the beers as a bonsella.

We ferry the team over the next day, go up in the evening and establish comms satisfactorily, and then settle into a routine of trying to keep away from the mopani flies, trying not to overheat, and getting to the Surf Club in front of the early evening rush to get a couple of cold beers before demand outstrips the cooling capacity of the freezer.

On the third day, just before lunch, there is the sound of an aircraft. Nobody is expecting visitors, so this is a big event in the day. Warracker and I get in a Land Rover and trundle out to the airstrip.

A civilian South African registered Hercules arrives creating an enormous dust storm amidst much screaming of propellers in reverse thrust. The rear ramp comes down and first out are a couple of tractors and a forklift, followed by a four-wheel drive – but brand new and gleaming. Fully laden pallets are pulled off, and finally two generators, that look as though they can quadruple the power available in Mukkers at a stroke.

Meanwhile, a fuel tanker has arrived, having been driven from Salisbury, escorted by police from Darwin down the escarpment and across the valley floor, arriving somewhat surprisingly unscathed.

The gennies are fuelled and fired up. One is connected to a couple of huge air compressors that start blowing up inflatable buildings. Within an hour, three inflatable buildings have materialised and are being rapidly cooled with massive mobile air conditioners. As the Herc leaves, a twin turboprop executive aircraft arrives. The door opens, and first at the top of the steps is the goddess Circe. Five stunning girls dismount, along with eight guys in jeans and chokers, cowboy hats, John Lennon style glasses and very limp-wristed handshakes. They've come to do a location shoot for some outfit in California, and are here for "However long it takes, buddy, we've got a darn good bud-jeet for this and we sure are gonna git the best sheeots of Africa we can".

Some of the people from the Herc have been left; they've brought everything with them including freezers, food, cooks and drivers. Mkumbura has grown an instant suburb.

Warracker makes sure that everybody knows everybody else. He doesn't actually claim to be the governor of the whole of the Zambezi valley, but that's the general impression left hanging in the air. Arrangements are made for sundowners at the Surf Club, and we're off for a quick 's, s and s' before coming to pick them up. Rob appears in a uniform festooned with wings, daggers and the rest, and, short of a hat with a feather in it, is starting to look the part of the governor. I'm going to have to rely on the fact that I've got a big watch to let them know who the aerial ace is, and just hope mummy didn't know any pilots and warn them that the bigger the watch, the smaller the chiloga.

The girls have scrubbed up even better than at first sight, and are quite happy to ride in the beaten up Land Rover, but the cowboys are wilting badly, and the few that come down to the club insist on going in their own air-conned truck.

Needless to say, they're an instant hit, the girls anyway, and they're actually good fun. A darts tournament is set up, and Tubbs and I partner two of the girls in a round robin. We have an overwhelming advantage, because Phil, who spends ninety-five per cent of the time clowning around, is actually a ringer, and is able to pull us out of the dwang at the last minute every time, so we win, which sends our two new best friends into screams of delight.

By this stage, the beers are starting to become warm, so the 'governor' suggests we take some back to the new suburb and get them in the deep freeze. The cowboys decide to stay on; they're in limp-wristed heaven, surrounded by real men who exist on a real frontier.

Back in tent city, the beer we've brought is redundant, as they've already got substantial supplies of wine chilled down which starts depleting at a healthy rate. The air conditioning is unbelievable. My darts partner is Cindy-Lou from Wyoming, who – like the others – has that straight-toothed, long-legged, healthy tanned look along with an IQ of almost a hundred. She apparently can't get one of her cases unlocked, so I become an instant suitcase engineer, and we wander off to her part of what is really an inflatable bungalow.

I manage to sort the case out; it's a combination lock and I think the fact that the magic numbers that open it are larger than three has confused her. She's very grateful, and I get a thank you kiss. Somehow our tongues get knotted together – the wine is doing its usual good work – and before long we're into trying to work out the colour of each other's underwear by touch only. I notice a frame beside the bed with a photo of a revoltingly good-looking guy with a very baleful look – he probably knew when the portrait was taken what it would be spending its life looking at. Cindy-Lou sees me looking at it, and I get an introduction. This is Duane. She's known him since college, it appears he's an ace at everything he tries his hand at, he's tall, fit, a football hero at college, a lawyer and they're getting married in the fall. She can't believe how anybody can be so happy, so much in love and so lucky. I start to panic; this is a really bad conversation. I'm desperately trying to think of ways to guide her away from this subject before she talks herself into fidelity, when with a sort of half shrug, smile and pout, Duane gets laid face down – he definitely knew, hence the baleful look – and we're quickly into a serious game of doctors and nurses.

I wake up in air-conditioned heaven. It's one of those so infrequent mornings when all the sports kit is geared up for an early morning workout, and there's actually a more than willing partner half an arm's length away. I can't believe my luck, but just as I'm getting all the pieces lined up, there's screaming and shouting and a very fearsome-looking Warracker appears in the door smothered with grenades, knives, pistols and his rifle – where does he keep all this stuff? – screeching that there's a contact close by and we have to get airborne. The only appropriate comment that springs to mind is borrowed from Captain Darling, of Blackadder fame, when he learns he's going over the top: "Bugger".

I'm in a real flap, getting untangled, being briefed by Rob as I'm hopping around trying to get my two-legged trousers onto my three-legged body; Cindy-Lou is sitting in bed with the sheet stuffed in her mouth, giggling and displaying two perfect advertisements for the milk-producing state, towards which Warracker is actually delivering the briefing. I manage to forget my pistol belt and survival kit.

We are airborne within a few minutes, with a face-blackened stick of warriors that have been conjured up from somewhere. The contact is about five minutes' flying time away; a truckload of police reservists has been ambushed and the fighting is still in progress. We arrive overhead, can't get much sense over the radio, but can see our guys deployed and delivering a great volume of fire into the bush to the north. From the air, the bush is pretty sparse and offers very little cover, but for the life of us we cannot identify any terrorists. We eventually get someone coherent on the radio who gives us some target identification and even fires a couple of mini-flares, telling us that's right on their position. We give it another look, and then being very careful to land behind the troops on the ground, go and have a chat with them. It takes a while to piece it together. The truck has definitely been fired on, there are about a dozen holes in it. Rob remarks that it is amazing nobody was wounded, but it's Phil who points out that it is outgoing rounds that have made the holes, not incoming. The whole truth doesn't emerge until later in the day, when somebody finally coughs up to having had a negligent discharge; several of his psyched-up mates, genuinely believing they were in an ambush, started firing as they were debussing, with several of the rounds hitting the truck from the inside; after that, with all the firing going on, it was easy to convince themselves they were in a mean firefight. Ho hum.

By the time I get back to recover my gun belt, the film team have disappeared off to work, and as I wander into the room, Duane has been reinstated and now has a very cocky, self-satisfied look on his face – how do they do that? I pick up my kit and am about to leave, but have a rummage round and find a pair of panties that I pull over the whole frame. That'll sort him out.

We go and watch some of the film shots being set up, which has to be one of the most bizarre sights I've ever seen. There are Africans wandering by with herds of goats, totally ignoring what's going on as though it were an everyday occurrence; the girls are in various scenarios with old mudallahs, snot-nosed kids, flies and the general detritus of tribal trust land living, looking as though they've just materialised from the pages of Vogue. And co-ordinating the whole shebang are these high-voiced, neurotic wimps in cowboy boots and bandanas.

We organise a repeat match for the evening, and after Tubbs has won the darts championship for us again, we get back to the ranch with the numbers mixed and matched to everybody's satisfaction. We've acquired the Special Branch representative, who'd missed last night's party but is as smooth as a snake, and a gawky national service troopie with pebble glasses and zits that one of the girls, to the disbelief of everybody, has latched on to. I'm later reliably informed that he is hung like a baboon.

Cindy-Lou is delighted with the pantie thing; she thinks

it is real whacky English humour, and Duane is condemned to spend the rest of his time in Mkumbura trying to peer through a light blue haze. I wish I'd used a pair from the laundry pile.

Meanwhile, Bax and his boys have carried out their attack successfully and have started their walk out. Life hasn't all been darts, drink and diddling; we've been airborne each early morning, middle of the day and late afternoon to establish VHF comms with the ground team. They are starting to have a water problem, and Rob gives them coordinates for a drum that was buried some weeks before in a previous exercise. Unfortunately, when they get there and dig it out, the water is unusable. They are getting in a bad way, so we start making plans to ferry them in a water resupply. As far as I am concerned, this is well within the rules of the briefing and doesn't need to be cleared elsewhere. For some reason, there don't appear to be any water jerrycans immediately available, which is hard to believe, but somebody hits on the plan of filling some large plastic bags with water and freezing them in the film camp's deepfreeze, then transporting them out in the helicopter as solid blocks.

We agree a rendezvous with Tim Bax and kick off early the next morning. Some of the bags are frozen solid, but some are still water. We pile them on board anyway and set off. Very quickly, a couple of the bags start leaking. As the helicopter flies nose down, the water runs forward, and the yaw pedals are soon under water. There's a massive leak somewhere, and as all this weight of water is moving forward, the centre of gravity changes, the nose wants to go down further, and I'm starting to run out of rearward movement on the stick. It is really quite funny; we're going to have to land having been brought down by a sack of water! In fact, I manage to fly the aircraft out of balance sideways for a bit – there are various of my previous instructors who might ask what's unusual about that – and we manage to spill enough out the side to arrive at the LZ in one go. We don't shut down, of course, but stay for about fifteen minutes; the team have a good drink and refill their bottles and some extras we've brought in the chopper. Tim and Rob have a good chinwag, and we take some of their kit into the helicopter, but the truth is they don't carry much that they don't actually need, so it's not a lot of help; the main thing they ditch is the HF radio and batteries, which are heavy and bulky, and considered superfluous as we have good VHF comms with them from the air. They look absolutely knackered, and still have a good three days before they'll be in a position to be lifted back over the minefield. The heat in this part of the valley is like a crematorium.

That evening, when we land after the radio sched, Rob tells me that they are making pretty slow progress, and suggests we do another water run on the following day. We have a laugh about borrowing some flippers so I can fly properly, and then the anomaly hits me: we're just about to settle into another air-conditioned wine tasting and these poor sods are conserving water for another day's hike. I tell him that we're not doing another water run, and to tell them in the morning call that they are to immediately find and secure an LZ for uplift. We'll take a couple of drums of fuel up to the crossing point, and we will have them out in four lifts by mid-morning. If we are going to be flying in and out with water, we may as well pre-empt the whole exercise and just hoik them out.

Rob is delighted but wants to know if this has to be confirmed with air force headquarters before he starts organising everything for their reception and onward movement. As far as I'm concerned, the decision has been made, and we can sort out the paperwork and authorisations when the fait accompli has been presented.

The lift goes off without a hitch. Rob has organised a Dakota to take them to the Scouts' base at Inkomo, so we ferry them to the airfield as well. But the downside is that this is the end of the detachment and it is time to reposition at Darwin. Cindy-Lou and I sort of arrange to try to get together in Salisbury when they come through, but I never see nor hear from her again. Ships that pass in the night. Or a shit that passed in the night as Duane might say. I like to think of him in Wichita Falls or wherever, lying awake wondering why his wife has had this curious habit throughout their married life of drying her underwear on the family photo frame.

Tubbs spends the rest of our tour at Darwin loudly complaining about the lack of air-con and chilled wine, and the rest of the fireforce is mightily pissed off because my first experience of 'real' Africa was so surreal. There is some muttering from Air Ops about our self-authorisation, but it's not really serious. I learned long ago to work on the principle of 'if you have to ask, you know it's wrong', and generally, once the thing's over, nobody is going to mind too much. The problem is that everybody knows and privately agrees what should be done. It should be a matter of policy, and not left to junior officers to make the decision – and thus be left with the responsibility if it all turns to rat shit. Luckily for the air force, it rarely does, but it is appalling that the staff allow the operators to shoulder these decisions without formulating a structure that allows them to do so legally.

CHAPTER THREE

Umtali

I get sent to Umtali, the border town with Mocambique. In recent weeks there have been an escalating series of 'incidents', firing on border patrols and the like. Ken Newman reports having some sort of missile fired at him whilst engaged on a casevac in the Vumba close to the border, and by the description it sounds like a SAM-7 rather than an RPG. It is obvious that Frelimo, the government of Mocambique, are psyching themselves up to join in the war more formally than just assisting ZANLA with transport and rear-holding bases.

We are based at Adam's Barracks, which dominate the high ground and are actually right on the border. They are also right next to Marymount School – a girls' boarding school. Just after I arrive I have afternoon tea with the headmistress and the local army commander. The headmistress voices her concerns about the proximity of her 'gels' to the teenage national servicemen in the barracks, but Andrew, the commander, tells her he is confident the barbed-wire topped chain link fence will keep the girls out of the cantonment. I decide that the best approach path to the landing pad happens to be over the school's outside pool, so there is always a pleasant few minutes sight-seeing at the end of each flight.

At breakfast one morning I am introduced to an interesting couple of characters who are in the process of 'proving' a new concept. They are leading a mounted infantry patrol of about ten men and horses through the mountains – and this eventually develops into the Grey Scouts, which gives a good account of itself as the war develops, particularly in the vast flatlands of the Repulse area when the war spreads there. We spend a pleasant week swanning around doing odd tasks for the police and army in the Vumba Mountains to the south and as far down as the beautiful Chimanimani at Melsetter, and Inyanga to the north. We even manage to wangle a night stop at Leopard Rock hotel when the weather clags late in the day. I receive a signal ordering me to position at the Penalongha Show, and we do a demonstration of trooping enplaning and deplaning exercises, including some of the troops roping down and hover jumping. Whilst the aircraft is on static display the national servicemen revel in the time-honoured fashion of soldiers in every time and place. The war has not yet come to this part of the country and soldiers and helicopters are still a novelty – it will not be many months before this becomes one of the most brutal battlegrounds of all, and the local population, often in isolated farmsteads, suffer many deaths and casualties.

Tony Jordan – the technician/gunner – fusses around like a mother hen making sure that the hordes of young boys who want to climb in and look around the chopper don't do any damage, and I occasionally go and give him a hand when some of the young mums and daughters need an explanation of how it all works. I decide that the terms of my task are broad enough to take some of the locals for a spin around the bay as 'good public relations'. In return, we get invited to stay for the evening braai and party – no complaints from the troops we've brought – so we end up staying the night, sleeping arrangements left to personal initiative. The illicit helicopter rides have put a lot of brownie points in the bank, and the judicious identification of who is unattached coupled with administration of the right amount of wine provide for a very pleasant night stop.

★

The following morning, shortly after landing back at Umtali, I am called to the army ops room and briefed on an incident that has occurred on the border to the north. The sitrep is pretty sparse, a PATU Land Rover is overdue and there are only intermittent and unintelligible comms with them: can we fly along the border and try to locate them?

We mount up and set sail northwards along the border, which is in fact a dirt road going north, along which the vehicle had been patrolling. Fifteen minutes later we receive a radio message, giving an approximate grid reference for the stick and the information that they have been ambushed from Mocambique and, although there are no casualties, they are dismounted from the vehicle and pinned down by enemy fire. Ten minutes later I get intermittent comms with the PATU stick and ask for an updated sitrep with their actual locstat. In response I get a high-speed, very garbled and over-excited babble, which is impossible to decipher. The guy won't let go of his transmit button, so I can't break in to calm him down, but the Becker Homer – a rudimentary radio homing device we can use to identify the direction of a radio transmission, which we generally use for locating SAS patrols in the featureless flatlands of the Zambezi valley – gives me a quick steer towards them. The actual border jigs in and out quite a lot here, I think joining up high points. I can see the abandoned vehicle some miles ahead, and instead of following the border, cut off several corners and fly to it directly.

The stick leader, who still hasn't take his finger off the transmit button, helpfully informs me that I am getting close to him as he can hear me but can't see me. His voice then rises several more octaves and he starts screaming that we are being fired at. We are already aware of this as there is the 'popping' of some pretty intensive small arms around the aircraft, which means it is close, but is not actually hitting us. I move back to our side of the border. I can't see anybody near the Land Rover and can't get a word in to the stick, although they are somewhere close by in the vicinity, obviously somewhere in the pine forest that comes up to the border. I find an LZ in dead ground, land and shut down, with the intention of getting a face to face briefing on the situation. By the time the blades have wound down, two policemen have materialised out of the trees and escort me up the hill whilst Tony stands guard over the helicopter.

There is a very steep climb of a couple of hundred metres up through the pine forest before we get to the stick leader and the rest of his men. They are all reservists and, apart from one, all over fifty or possibly older. They are 'dug-in' in rudimentary shell scrapes and using the tree trunks as cover, but are completely disorientated as they are facing ninety degrees away from the border and the direction of the enemy fire. Apparently, having come under fire, the vehicle stalled so they debussed, and every time they have tried to get back to the vehicle they have come under intense fire. I suggest we snivel up to a vantage point a little away from the landie so that they can point out exactly where the enemy is, but once we are there it becomes obvious they have no actual idea of where the fire is coming from other than 'Mocambique', of which we are visual with vast swathes. My own personal weapon is a nine mill Czech sub-machine gun, so I borrow an FN and start firing into likely positions, ignoring the whingeing about their having to account for the ammunition. I hit the jackpot on the third choice and the bad guys return a severe snottie. I mark the position on my map and we withdraw into dead ground.

The plan is for us to lift and fly to the north. After a while I'll cross into Mocambique and eventually come over the firing position from the rear. Whilst we engage them the police are to get to the vehicle, not waste time trying to start it and roll it backwards into cover.

Tony Jordan gets the gun ready; we only have a 7.62 MAG machine gun, and we get airborne and depart. We do some nap-of-the-earth flying and get right onto the Freds from behind before Tony gets stuck in with the MAG and they realise we're there. He drops several of them as they scatter before they start returning fire. It is close but not actually hitting us, but we are starting to get regular stoppages so it is good to see the agreed signal – a red flare – that the Land Rover is clear and we can break contact. We fly by the waving PATU stick and trog off home.

All in all, a pretty unremarkable incident. Or it would have been until two days later when I received a signal to take the helicopter to the town airstrip and meet an air force Kiwit – Cessna 185 – and pick up two visiting officers. They're both wing commanders and I assume they are on some sort of staff visit, so am a little nonplussed when, after getting back to the barracks, I discover they are having not quite a board of enquiry but a mini investigation into why I have escalated the border tension with an 'unprovoked aggressive airstrike'. I explained the situation, and that we had been fired upon, and am astounded to be asked:

"Were the bullets coming close?"

"Does it matter? If somebody shoots at me, he is very definitely not my friend. And if you can hear them, they're close enough."

From radio intercepts, it has been ascertained that there were several casualties and some kills, and they are not amused by my comment that Tony was shooting well. It is not quite a bollocking; I am counselled to be more circumspect in reacting to such incidents, as, "We're not at war with these people you know", and we have another pot of tea and some biscuits before they start on their way back to Salisbury.

It turns out that they are right only briefly; a day or so later Frelimo announces that Mocambique is now in a state of war with Rhodesia.

★

A new FAF is opened a few miles to the west of Umtali. We go there for the first time before any work on the infrastructure has started – arriving in the gloom of low cloud and rain rolling in off the Vumba mountains, surrounding the bowl in which the town is situated. There are some basic revetments of earth-filled oil drums to protect the helicopters in the event of an attack, and the aircrew already there have sleeping bags rolled out on the floor in an old two-storey house that doubles up as an ops room, the air traffic tower, kitchen and eating area, with a very tiny room converted to the all-important bar. We have a quick handover/takeover with the outgoing fireforce commander, bed the aircraft down and get our personal space squared away in a spare corner of the living accommodation. It is already dark and we squeeze into the bar a couple of beers behind the others, who already have a bit of flying speed on. One of the other gunners is Phil Tubbs, whom I have flown with previously on my rugged deployment to Mukumbura amongst the American advertising crew, but this is the first time I meet the other half of the legendary 'Jarvie and Tubbs' duo, who are hardly ever mentioned as separate entities. They are the subject of innumerable tales and instigators of as many pranks. Henry has recently rejoined the air force, or perhaps is just having his service extended; I know he had been off the squadron for some months as there has been some administrative hiccup with his being either promoted to, or continuing in the rank of, flight sergeant. Anyway, here he is, looking so scrawny that you feel if he turns sideways there will be no shadow, despite his being wrapped in several layers of pullovers and flying jackets against the damp cold. I recall a remark that Ginger Morris, one of the other gunners, made to me describing a boxing match with Henry – they had both been contenders for a place in the Rhodesian Olympic boxing team before the country was banned from participating. He reckoned that Henry hit him so hard and so fast he thought he was surrounded.

Although nominally in charge of this little detachment, I am still – in fact, always will be – considered to be the new boy from Mud Island, with some strange ways of doing things and a strange way of speaking. Wherever I go, about three-quarters of the personnel I've never met before, but invariably, Rhodesia having such a small white community, and the air force even smaller, they have all been to the same schools or sports clubs or are related by marriage, and look very guardedly at this outsider in their midst.

About an hour later, the hubbub of noise in the small room starts to abate, and increasing attention is being given to an altercation between Henry and Phil. Although aware of it at the other end of the bar, I'm not interested in any way – it seems to be about their relative skill as darts throwers and is progressing through beer chugging to sexual prowess. However, as their volume increases the rest of the room slowly drop their own conversations to enjoy the enfolding spectacle and they become the only performance in the cabaret. As often happens between beer-fuelled mates, what had started as a mild disagreement seems to be taking on a more serious and belligerent aspect. There are a couple of half-hearted attempts by some of the other NCOs to break it up. I am still only half interested when one of the other pilots says:

"Hey, Mike, you're the senior guy here, you'd better break

this up." I'm reluctant to play the heavy hand, but things suddenly escalate when Hajj slaps Phil on the cheek. Now there is complete silence. Phil now does a double slap on Henry. I groan inwardly; I don't want this on my watch. They are now slapping each other – not nastily, more like a couple of eight-year old schoolgirls in a playground, but I obviously can't let a fight develop. I suppose I delay in intervening in the hope that one of the Rhodesian officers will step in, and luckily that is my saving grace as, just before I move, the slaps turn into the 'William Tell Overture' and there are roars of laughter all round. Henry had decided that Tubbs should introduce us, but wanted to check out if I was a stuffed-shirt Brit first. He's lost the bet that I would play the 'I'm the officer here, now you lads behave yourself' card and would now be buying the beer for the rest of the evening. He doesn't realise just how close he has come to winning. He becomes one of my greatest friends, one of the gunners I prefer from choice to fly with, and a magnificent man. I am devastated when he is shot down and killed two years later.

★

The terrain in the Eastern Districts is very different to that in the Hurricane area. It is characterised by rugged mountains whose lower slopes are covered in thick bush. Tactics have to be modified and after Op Thrasher, which is the name given to the area, commences, there are no early successes for the fireforce despite a large number of callouts. We spend a period of five days where we are seemingly constantly airborne, arriving at a succession of vehicle ambushes, sightings of terrorist groups and other incidents, always long after the gooks have departed.

We return from a dawn scramble to a farmhouse attack the previous night and the crews are in a very disgruntled mood. On arrival at the scene, we had discovered that the attack had been a fleeting engagement at last light the previous night; the group of terrorists had discontinued firing and moved off as soon as the farmer had returned fire. A police PATU unit had arrived by vehicle at the farm shortly afterwards and was deployed around the homestead, assuring us that they had not requested assistance from the fireforce. Our fireforce troops are not RLI, but an RR company, inexperienced in fireforce operations but very keen and diligent in preparing themselves with enplaning and deplaning drills and operating in liaison with the K-Car once on the ground. The surfeit of lemons has at least given them a grace period of on-the-job training. It is obvious, however, that the fireforce is being grossly misused. This has happened before, and has to be guarded against whenever a fireforce is moved into an area with troops and particularly JOC commanders who have not had access to one before. They often see it as the solution to all their problems and want to send aircraft here, there and everywhere. The military in general, and the army in particular, hate seeing people sitting around doing nothing, and sometimes it has to be explained that having the aircraft and crews together on instant standby is not a waste of assets, but ensures that you can apply maximum force when it is required: aircraft, crews and troops armed, cocked and in one place.

It is time to have a chat with the operations commander at the JOC headquarters, which is still in the town, Umtali, waiting to move out to the airfield. I grab the army company commander, tell the other crews that we'll maintain a listening watch on the appropriate radio frequency and fly into town to have a chat with the colonel. I explain to him that the concept of fireforce is not to fly willy-nilly around the countryside burning holes in the sky and wearing out the crews, but to react to very specific incidents. Generally this is when terrorists are in a static position being observed by our own troops, a contact is in progress and the troops can maintain contact until we arrive, or in response to high-grade intelligence, generally provided by a Selous Scouts pseudo team or ground coverage elements of the police Special Branch.

It turns out that things were even worse than we'd imagined. The colonel has been away in Salisbury for the last couple of days, his deputy has been more interested in the logistics of the move out to the FAF than organising the war and we have essentially been deployed – chasing our tails around the area – on the say-so of a woman corporal of the RWS employed in the ops room to mark up the maps. Bags of initiative, not much sense. We get the ground rules sorted out and fly back to Grand Reef, where, without Miss Itchy Finger near the scramble button, we now sit for four days without a single callout.

If there is one thing worse than too much flying, it is no flying, so on Sunday, when an opportunity presents itself, we jump at the chance. Captain Morgan-Davies, the troops' company commander, is catching up on his admin and isn't so keen. The local SB policeman has arrived at the camp with a village headman. The headman claims that there is a terrorist encampment in the bush by his village and he is fed up with their demands for food to be prepared for them and their pestering of the young women in his kraal. He has brought this information to the police in response to one of the posters that are displayed around the various stores and towns in the rural areas offering quite substantial rewards for information, and bounty money for terrorists killed or captured and weapons recovered. Although this is a potentially lucrative opportunity for tribesmen, there is a deadly price for them and their families to pay if even a suspicion of their being a 'sell-out' came to the terrorists' ears. Punishments culminate in a grisly, slow and painful death – as 'an example to the masses' – and normally include having ears, lips, and noses removed, cooked by one of the wives and then eaten, either by the miscreant himself or one of his wives or children, before his final despatch.

The normal response now would be for an OP (observation post) to be established or a reconnaissance team put into the area to corroborate the information, but the SB guy reckons the headman's information has stood up pretty well to close questioning about the camp. To me, he also seems confident about locating his village on the map, which is unusual; most African villagers have great difficulty matching the abstract details of a map with their mental picture of the area it refers to. I want the guys to fly and shake a few moths out anyway, so the long and short of it is that M-D allocates two sticks to us and, as he is staying behind, we put the policeman and the headman in the spare seat of the K-Car. The skinny headman looks as though a strong wind will blow him away, so we make sure he is belted in against the rotor wash. There is little weight penalty and he ends up half on and half off the seat, facing forwards next to me and the policeman, with his legs dangling out the door, primarily as an interpreter. Basically, it will be a Sunday afternoon 'jolly' under the auspices of an exercise. A study of the map shows that we can approach using terrain masking for noise cover from the north, and the two obvious escape routes for any gooks would be to run either north or south along the riverbed that runs alongside the village. I brief the two G-Car pilots to find their own LZs respectively north and south along this river and deploy their troops independently before going into a wide orbit around the village, whilst we will climb up and see if this villager can locate the supposed camp. It is all in slow time – nobody has any real faith in the intelligence – we have lunch, get our sports gear on and amble off for a Sunday afternoon constitutional.

As we approach the village, I am surprised that the headman readily recognises the two small hill features just to the north of his village from this highly unusual perspective, in what must be, for him, an incredible experience. I hear Dave Atkinson calling on the radio that he has found an LZ and is deploying his stick in the riverbed to the north as we pull up over the village, the headman chattering away excitedly about seeing his huts from the air. It is a peaceful African village scene, some people strolling through the huts, a few children running around, dogs disturbed by the sudden appearance of the aircraft and women working on the edge of a stream, the brightly coloured clothes they have been washing laid out on the rocks to dry.

We start into a second orbit and I notice the other G-Car out of the corner of my eye heading past the village towards his LZ to the south.

"Sir, sir, there's something up," from Henry. The women are gathering their belongings and heading for cover. This is a good sign. When we arrive at a location, if the locals generally carry on about their normal business it is an indication that they don't think a firefight is about to commence – i.e. there are no gooks around. If they start high-stepping it out of the way, they are expecting a lot of bullets to be flying around in the near future. Not infallible, but a little piece of jigsaw in the puzzle of assessing the situation.

And then, suddenly, there they are: figures dressed in dark denim lugging weapons and packs and scurrying furtively from rock to rock, using all available cover. So far they have had the sense not to open fire; there is still hope that we haven't seen them. They have obviously been down in the kraal and are now trying to ease back into the bush.

"Off you go, Jarvs." Henry lets down four or five bursts of twenty mill. There are immediate bright flashes as the rounds, which are high-explosive incendiary, burst amongst the groups of terrorists. On hitting hard surfaces they explode and fragment into hundreds of small pieces of hot shrapnel. Several terrorists collapse on the rock and the rest start to run, some returning small arms fire in our direction. The survivors of the first strike all move towards the stream we had identified and break into two groups, the smaller turning right and heading north up the riverbed, the larger group going south.

There are about five in the small group and Henry slams a number of bursts into their group. Some fall and lie still and others disappear into cover. I rack the aircraft around violently to position ourselves going south rather than turning in an orbit, and we start picking them off running down the river like a strung-out group of runners in a cross-country race. Chris Dickinson in the southern helicopter calls and says he is having trouble finding an LZ and I tell him to get over the river and get the troops out quick as the fastest survivors of the initial attacks are almost down to his position. He hover-jumps the stick out right over the riverbed from about ten feet as the first terrorist appears running towards him and they are in immediate contact, but the breakout has been contained both ways and we have the whole group in a relatively small area with ourselves above it.

Some of the terrorists run back away from the contact with the stick on the ground but choose to stay in the riverbed. On the ground it probably gives good cover, but they are likely unaware that there are only two sticks of troops deployed and they would do better to break across the open ground and into the thicker cover. We would drop a few but some would almost certainly make it. Anyway, they choose to stay in the riverbed where we can see the movement from above and we put down some more bad news on their way back, before the situation stabilises.

I tell Henry to put some rounds down on each of the many bodies lying on the rock and in the riverbed; it is a favourite tactic of the gooks to play dead and then ease away when attention is directed elsewhere. Whilst this is going on I start to organise the G-Cars, one to stay in a wide orbit to discourage any breakout, and the other to go and refuel before returning in order that there is always an aircraft on hand for casevac duty or for quickly repositioning a stick of soldiers. I also give a warning order to the two stop groups, telling the northern group to get into a good blocking position and the southern to prepare to commence sweeping northwards up the river with two men on either bank. They will flush out any enemy in cover and either deal with them, drive them into the other stop group's position, or cause them to break out into the open where they will be an easy shot for us. The headman and SB guy are jabbering away in Shona, and the policeman tells me that the headman is really impressed with the show so far but says that we have missed one of the m'unungugwa (terrorists) who is hiding under a fallen tree trunk on the river bank. We have a close look but can see nothing. I tell Henry to put a burst down right next to it, and to our surprise a denim-clad figure leaps up and starts to run. The next burst nails him.

The headman then tells us that there are two hiding under a thick piece of bush and when we fire, sure enough we get another two. This character, as well as being completely at home in the strange and noisy environment which senior infantry officers take many sorties to become comfortable with, throughout the frantic, bewildering and fast-moving opening few minutes of an air-to-ground engagement, has not only not been overwhelmed or terrified by the experience, but is thoroughly enjoying it and has kept track of the position below us.

He informs us that one of the bodies we had put a second burst on was shamming, and sure enough when we put a third down, it miraculously recovers and starts to move away before we drop it again.

The sweep of our own stick commences, and Op Thrasher's

first fireforce 'kill' is a hundred percent score. Not the ideal situation, as it would have been good to have had a couple of prisoners, but at least we have broken our duck. The only minor blemish from our point of view comes in the last contact when the last surviving terrorists run into the northern stop group. Dave Atkinson flies overhead to put down some machine-gun fire whilst we are refuelling and the terrorists fire at the helicopter. One round bounces off the top of the cyclic stick and is stopped by Dave's cigarette lighter and another goes through both of the gunner's feet – he sits with them outside the left door of the helicopter, and one must have been resting on top of the other. It is a clean hole and although quite painful, after having it cleaned up and dressed by some fluttery-eyed nurses at Umtali hospital, he is not even sent back to Salisbury but is flying the next day.

When we finally arrive back at Grand Reef – we all land at the hospital, of course, which is why we know about the fluttering eyes – Morgan-Davies is beside himself with jealousy and frustration at having missed the show, and the two sticks of young national serviceman – who are not, of course, the A team first wave of choice – revel in their status as instant heroes.

In theory, the headman has become a very rich man in an afternoon. I hope they paid him all the money due to him and that he and his family survived to enjoy it.

At this stage of the war, the terrorist groups did not enjoy anywhere near the support of the majority of the rural population, who were quite often pro-government. In general, those who worked hard improved their lot and led comfortable lives. Rather like civilian populations in most terrorist conflicts, they were not particularly enamoured or interested in the politics of either side. The Rhodesian government missed a golden opportunity in not nurturing this latent loyalty in the tribal trust lands, and chose to believe that the blacks were not to be deeply trusted, despite the spectacular loyalty and courage shown by our own African troops in the Scouts, RAR and Special Branch, and indeed, by a lot of the civilian black population. As time progressed the people in the rural areas were forced to offer succour to insurgents, not as idealistic converts but simply because the government was neither encouraging them to do otherwise nor protecting them from the terrorist atrocities perpetrated to recruit them.

Talking to African friends of mine after the war, I was told that a lot of blacks had voted for Mugabe and ZANU not because they thought he would improve their lot or that it was the right way for the country to develop, but simply because it appeared to be the only way to get the war stopped so they could get back to their previous quiet way of life.

Dave Atkinson, a former junior Springbok swimmer, is an amazing fellow, who many years later became a helicopter squadron commander in Mugabe's Zimbabwean air force. He is hugely overweight, and during a scramble callout moves at a fast waddle to his aircraft, but is as brave as a lion. It is a mystery how he passes his flying medical each year, as he smokes like the proverbial chimney, drinks prodigious amounts of beer each and every evening without fail – the first cold beer after flying hardly touches the side of his throat – normally rounded off with a bottle of brandy, or if unavailable, vodka, before tucking-in in his jim-jams. I share a cabin with him and often drift to sleep to the extraordinary noises that his body produces – it cannot be dissimilar to bedding down with a hippopotamus. However, definitely one of the people you want to have on your side, both professionally and socially, and, as he says: "People mustn't tell me not to smoke. This lighter saved my life."

CHAPTER FOUR

Who Needs a Nosewheel?

We are detached to Marymount mission in the northeast of the country to support an SAS operation. Head honcho of the mission, somewhat strangely, is a former Luftwaffe pilot who is completely anti the security forces. Previously he wouldn't allow the soldiers to use the pool at the mission, but during a visit by the new Minister of Defence one of the troopies raised this subject and the missionary was made an offer he couldn't refuse: if he wanted to stay with his flock in this part of the world, the troops get to use the pool after standing down each day. I have been here previously with Henry Jarvie and Phil Tubbs and have a sort of neutral relationship with the German; mainly we stay off the contentious issues and talk about aeroplanes. On our previous visit, we spent hours teaching the sisters at the mission to play poker. They accepted that there is no point in playing the game if no money is involved and got some sort of dispensation to enable them to gamble. We are using matchsticks as chips and at the end of five days have accumulated about ten thousand. Unfortunately, the exchange rate has been set at about one cent equal to a couple of hundred matches, so the spoils are a few bottles of coke. Unfortunately, my gunner for this trip is DB. He is an excellent technician, but we are not compatible – not only does he not drink, which is his own business, but when he does appear in the bar he has short arms and deep pockets, so it is difficult to establish a social rapport. He doesn't like pilots in general, and after a few days together I have been relegated to the bottom of his Christmas card list. On the way out from Salisbury he announces that he is checking my map reading, which quickly develops into a one-sided conversation on who does what in the aircraft, and during our initial few days at Mukumbura the helicopter becomes two-tone after he cleans 'his' half of the aircraft. We don't even have a discussion about who does what on the ground – his job is to look after the aircraft, screw the panels up, put the right fluids in the right holes, wipe all the bits that need wiping and understand all those technical things, and mine is to be the pilot, which involves keeping my maps tidy, my hair sleek and shiny and drinking copious amounts of beer whilst looking casual and heroic leaning against the Surf Club bar. He's lucky one of the things he doesn't have to wipe is my nose – judging from the age of the new arrivals on the squadron, the techs might soon have to start doing that. If he'd seen how organised my map case was or the state of my car, he'd never have thought I could be shamed into cleaning 'my' half of the helicopter. He finally gives up when I scrape a clear space from the crud on the Plexiglas in front of me in order to see where I am going, and now the helicopter is kept clean all over.

The SAS are extremely professional. We are there to provide hot extraction support for a fighting patrol that is already deployed over the border. We are fully briefed on the operation in progress and then the local situation – this is, after all, an outpost in Indian country. In the event of the camp being attacked, we are to stay in our basha unless specifically escorted out by one of the soldiers. All of the soldiers have their own specific arcs of fire and responsibility in the event of the camp being attacked, and the last thing they want is a couple of aircrew galloping around in the middle of the night. The helicopter is pushed into a revetment made from empty fuel drums filled with earth as anti-rocket protection, and overhead wire netting to minimise any direct mortar hit damage. An attack starts just after midnight with a mortar barrage, and is sustained for about an hour with small arms, RPGs and several more barrages of mortars. I get my boots and survival belt on and cock my pistol and sub-machine gun. DB is making moves to get out of the bunker but I remind him of our instructions. As there is nothing else to do, I lie down and drift back to sleep. This astounds the troopie who comes to collect us once the attack is finished, but as far as I'm concerned there was nothing else to do. We are escorted to the commanding officer. There are no casualties and only superficial damage to our camp but there has been a simultaneous attack on a nearby territorial force camp and they have some casualties in need of casevac if possible. Whilst the helicopter is being readied and I am planning the trip to the casevac loc I watch a small patrol led by Captain Martin Pearce slip out of the mission gates. They are on their way to exact retribution and, sure enough, in the morning they have three bodies, a mortar tube and several other bits of discarded terrorist kit, having bumped the perpetrators celebrating prematurely a few clicks away. The last thing they had expected was any immediate follow up. We get airborne and transit to the other camp. The moon has set and it is very dark, but the soldiers on the ground have used vehicle lights to illuminate an LZ. For once it is lined up the right way into wind. We make a long gradual descent to the LZ and as I am coming into the hover just short of the landing, I catch some movement in my peripheral vision and there is a gigantic blinding flash on the landing area directly in front of us. My first thought is that we are being mortared. My night vision has been destroyed completely and I haul in collective and climb fast straight ahead. I know there are hills in front of us, but I don't want to start turning in case it causes me to get disorientated. Finally, things get organised – we are above the high ground and established in a gentle level turn a bit away from the camp and my vision is restoring. There is no indication of any further explosions, and the reason becomes apparent with a radio call from the company commander. A troopie decided it would be helpful for us to have more illumination and has thrown an instant light grenade out in front of us. I establish that he is safely out of the way and there are no other benevolent assistants around the LZ before agreeing to make a fresh approach and landing. Whilst we are waiting on the ground for the two stretcher cases to be loaded, we can see that this attack has caused a lot more damage. There are several soldiers walking around with fresh dressings, and much evident shrapnel damage to buildings and vehicles. But it is also apparent that not much thought had been given to anti-mortar protection in the form of reinforced bunkers and revetments for the trucks. The following night we get a call from the SAS patrol in Mocambique. In the process of a night attack on a terrorist camp they have taken a gunshot casualty and would like us to come and pull him out. It is, of course, as black as the proverbial witch's, but the squadron never asks unless it is really necessary so, not without some misgivings, we set off over the border on a heading towards the patrol's given grid reference. The patrol is led by Drive Wilson, later to become the last commander of C Squadron, and the most highly decorated soldier of the war. Despite the fact he is a very large man, on first meeting you think he's a schoolteacher. He wears a pair of gold wire spectacles that he is continuously pushing back onto the bridge of his nose – an identifying mannerism copied by his soldiers, but only behind his back. He is quietly spoken and mild-mannered among strangers, but is a very tough man indeed, a strict professional and an animal when there is a party in progress. I am flying on 'time and heading', and about five minutes prior to the calculated time for arriving with the troops, I give them a call on the radio. We establish good comms straight away and I ask if they can hear the helicopter, to which the answer is no. As they are, for obvious reasons, reluctant to advertise their position with lights until they have to, the idea is that if we are close enough for them to hear us then they can show their position and the whole exercise can be completed and as much distance as possible put in before the enemy comes investigating. Shortly afterwards, Wilson tells me that they can hear us to their south-west and we seem to be heading towards them; there will be a short delay and he'll light the position. It remains black for a worrying number of minutes. I doubt they will want to use a bright strobe light so am searching in the darkness for a group of shrouded torches directed along our heading. There is a glow ahead which suddenly breaks into a fire, followed by another a little distance away, and quickly, several more. My immediate thought is mortar fire again, but then I see that Wilson has deployed his troops and they have been waiting for the order to ignite a small fire each, producing a flare path leading to the actual landing position marked by a 'T' of five small fires. It is like landing at Heathrow. Needless to say, the 'T' is directly into wind, each fire of the flare path is extinguished immediately as we pass it, the casevac is right by the LZ and we are ready to take off within thirty seconds of landing. We need the 'T' as a reference when lifting off, but as I go through transition climbing away, I notice it is immediately extinguished behind me. As I commence a climbing turn back towards the border, I call Wilson to sign off, and he tells me they are already on the move. A very, very slick operation. They continue their harassing operations inside Mocambique, but Frelimo are starting to bump them more and more often and they begin to head back towards the border. It becomes apparent that the area they must pass through has been saturated with troops to try to ambush them, and they are soon conducting a continuous fighting withdrawal. The SAS have requested extra helicopters in order that the whole patrol can be extracted, but they are not immediately forthcoming and there are signals flying backwards and forwards about 'unattributable operations', 'political ramifications of Rhodesian aggression', 'considerations of using high-value assets' and the like. The Rhodesian government is obsessed with the fairy tale that if aircraft are not used, the world won't think it is us that is cavorting around Mocambique ambushing convoys, attacking garrisons and blowing up arms dumps. Meanwhile, the patrol's situation is deteriorating rapidly and we devise a plan to start extracting them using one helicopter until the arrival of the others. At best we will get another three helicopters, which means we can lift sixteen off in one go. There are thirty-one guys on the ground, one having been casevaced a few nights previously, so the plan is to establish a refuelling point just on our side of the minefield and I will fly out with a minimum fuel load and lift off four at a time, refuelling the minimum required for the next trip, until such time as the others arrive. The exercise commences and the first sticks are lifted away. They are now in constant contact with the troops chasing them. We devise a pattern where they stand and settle into a static firefight with their pursuers, break contact and run hard when we are about ten minutes away in order that there are no enemy forces around the LZ whilst we are in the vulnerable positions of approach, landing and take-off. It works well, but there are Freds all over the place and we keep taking fire on each trip from groups scattered between the patrol and the border. We've got down to sixteen guys left over the way and we have a rethink. They don't want to leave an unviable fighting force on the ground. There is still no decision as regards extra helicopters.

Ammunition is also becoming an issue, so we take in a limited resupply on the next trip. Then disaster strikes. The refuelling point is a reasonably confined area LZ amongst some fairly tall trees. Due to the weight of the SAS troopers we cannot establish a high hover and let down slowly into the hole. I have been judging the approach and flare above the trees so that we sink into the hole and a progressive pull on the collective cushions each landing. I get it wrong, the descent accelerates and we thunder into the ground. There is a loud cracking sound and the nose starts to drop even further. I manage to level the nose by moving the cyclic backwards – a bit of a no-no, as it is easy to cause the main rotors to strike the tail boom when doing this – and establish a very low hover. By this time the troops have debussed and moved well away from us. DB gets out and has a look underneath, then reappears and signals me to shut down. I shake my head and indicate for him to connect himself back onto the intercom. As I had feared, I have snapped the nose wheel oleo, and he tells me that we must shut down as the aircraft is now u/s. I tell him to get out and get underneath, take some panels off and tell me if there is any internal damage – specifically to the main control linkages which are in the vicinity, and meanwhile to get the SAS commander to come and plug into the intercom. Whilst DB is working under the aircraft I explain to Martin Pearce what has happened. He tells me that the air request for more helicopters has been turned down but they have now upgraded it to a 'life or death' request as things have turned pear-shaped for the guys over the border and they are in deep serious doo-doo. The reinforcement choppers cannot be here effectively until last light at the earliest which probably means no extraction until the morning. DB reappears and says that there doesn't appear to be any damage to the control rods but I must shut down as he is not prepared to certify the aircraft as fit to fly. I tell him to wind his neck in and dismantle the nosewheel and then get fuel in whilst I hold the hover. He starts to give me a lecture on serviceability and the legalities of continuing to fly. The SAS officer starts to reason with him about the peril the men over the way are in, but I cut him short, explain to DB in words of one syllable that I'll take care of the paperwork and as long as I don't shut down the aircraft it has not technically been put u/s, and to get his arse into gear as I am getting tired holding the hover. He is extremely hacked off, but gets to work and Martin Pearce, the SAS officer and I start concocting a plan. It comes to a choice of two: do I start lifting troops back in to reinforce the patrol or do we carry on taking them out which means depleting the numbers even further? Unfortunately, we cannot bring Wilson into the debate as they are out of VHF radio range, and being on the run they will probably only listen out when they hear the helicopter. They are probably wondering where we are now, as it has been some time since the last lift. I decide that instead of leaving four men on their own for the last evolution, I'll take five men out this time and we'll see how well the gearbox was made with a final lift of seven, having got them to discard as much weight as they can – we've already lightened everything possible out of the helicopter, including tools, refueller and all the odds and sods of equipment, ammunition and the like. I am tempted to dismantle the machine gun and offer the gunner the opportunity to stay behind when he comes on the intercom and tells me the wheel is off and the panels taped in position, but he says he is coming, and it would be wrong to then take the gun off. The first lift goes reasonably well. I brief Drive on the way in and he tells me they have broken contact for the time being, but their position will obviously be compromised when we land. We take a fairly heavy burst of small arms from a group of Freds on the way in, and pass their location on to our guys as this is obviously a bad place for them to head towards. I tell them not to bugger about trying to read me on to their position by giving left/right corrections as we are running in, as I do not want to be manoeuvring at low speed and altitude with a lot of hostile fire around, and to just throw smoke so I can see them and do a fast approach with a big flare and landing at the end. The five pax are aboard very quickly and I start hauling in power to get airborne. There is a maximum contingency setting which we can pull for two seconds for emergency use and I go straight to this. As I clear the jessie bush I push in a lot of left yaw pedal, which takes power off the tail rotor and gets us going, accelerating very slowly but satisfactorily. Unfortunately, we stagger over another group of Freds but in fact don't take too much fire, as they are all ducking and scurrying for cover. They probably think we are taking aggressive action against them and are about to land right in amongst them. Wilson confirms that they have heard the firing and will not be moving in that direction either. I politely decline his request that we fly in a few concentric circles around his position to locate all the bad guys by drawing fire. DB grumbles a bit about what this is doing to the gearbox, but by this time he realises we are committed and we get the minimum of fuel on and are on our way back in double quick time. It is only when he follows the radio transmission that he twigs we are picking up seven this last time, and starts whingeing big time. The guys have discarded just about all their kit and booby trapped it, bar rifles, a couple of magazines each and one radio. I tell them that the last two to board will have to stand on the step outside and hang on, and that their mates must also hold onto them as if anybody gets shot and falls off we will not have the power to stop and pick them up. We take no fire going in but just as the troops are loading the lead elements of the pursuing force appear at the edge of the LZ and start firing. The nose is on a heading about ninety degrees away from the Freds and there is a bit of space in the LZ to accelerate using the cushion of air between the helicopter and the ground so we get going pretty easily, given that the power we are using is way beyond the design limits. A new problem has manifested itself, however, as the centre of gravity of the helicopter is now out of limits too far forward and the cyclic stick is back against the stop. I have no more collective to pull in, and no more movement in the cyclic to raise the nose so we are not gaining any height to clear the bush in front. There is obviously no way we can land and sort this problem out so I scream to DB to get the soldiers to lean as far to the rear as they can and for the two chaps on the outside to move as far back as they can. I have got some lateral movement of the cyclic and aim the aircraft at a gap where the bush is thinner and we explode through it with the rotors chopping branches, which are flying everywhere. I manage to keep us away from hitting any of the main trunks, and we are away, but limited to a sort of fast air taxi across the tops of the trees as I cannot let the cyclic forward to increase the speed. I am able to let some of the collective power off, but the gearbox has not made any groaning noises and subsequent checks – in truth the thing has to be overhauled – show that there was in fact no damage, which is a remarkable testament to its manufacture. We get close to the border and I agree with Drive that we will land and drop four of them off, ferry the others over the fence, and then return to pick them up. Pearce has already moved a security party right up to our own side of the fence. These guys think of everything. When we finally get everyone back into our own playground, the reception party has organised a couple of crates and some sandbags and ask if we can rest the nose on these. I ask DB what he thinks – it is not quite so simple as it might seem, as only certain parts of the airframe are stressed to take loads, but he hops out whilst we are hovering, rearranges the structure and carefully marshals me over it. There is a lot of fiddly minor hovering adjustments before he is satisfied – he is probably getting his own back making me do these minor corrections and I cannot blame him – I've been giving him a hard time all afternoon and in between time he's been taken around Indian country being deliberately exposed to a whole group of people intent on killing him – and I rest the nose gingerly on the mount and carefully bring the rotors to a standstill. It is the first time I have been able to take my hands off the controls for nearly three hours. I have deliberately left the engine going as I want to make sure there is no nonsense about signing off the aircraft, but there is no more whingeing on those lines. I think everybody concerned is just relieved and disbelieving that we are all here and unscathed. The SAS get a signal off for Mtoko to make arrangements to receive us in about an hour's time, explaining the problem and to have a mounting of mattresses on which I can rest the nose. The C Squadron guys seem to be impressed but DB never flies with me again, and a clique of the technicians then apparently refuse to fly with me, which I don't find out for a while. DB eventually becomes a civilian helicopter pilot, which shows some sort of anomaly in his thinking – who on earth would actually volunteer, let alone pay, for becoming a helicopter pilot? The machines are a contradiction in the principles of aerodynamics – they have two rotors, the main and tail, producing thrust along lines that are at right angles to each other. And the direction you move in is then perpendicular to both of those lines of thrust. How efficient is that? People have different ways of persuading the things to keep up the battle against gravity. My method is to feed in a constant series of control inputs, on the basis that if enough errors are produced they cancel each other out. It seems to work most of the time, and when it doesn't, the machinery is so confused it gives me time to think of Plan B.

CHAPTER FIVE

Starry Stevens

The boss, Squadron Leader Harold Griffiths, comes to Mtoko as part of his annual visit around the forward air fields. He announces that he will fly one of the G-Cars, is to be treated as any other pilot and then will probably take over as the detachment leader and K-Car driver in a few days when he has found his feet. I smile and tell him that he is yellow four and, as it happens, that is the duty pilot for the following morning and there is a first light task. The lips tighten a little, but he notes the details of the task.

We have recently received a stern warning regarding damage to the main rotor blades during recent start-ups. The engine is started and when fired up and ready, the main rotor blades are engaged through a clutch system. One of the checks before starting is that the blades are not over the engine exhaust as they are damaged by the heat, and this effect is made much worse with our aircraft because of the anti-strella shroud which deflects the full blast upwards. Several blades have been roasted, and as they come in matched sets of three this has caused some very expensive maintenance. The edict is that the next episode will result in the culprit being charged with negligence.

In a half sleep, I am aware of Griff getting up next door in the morning and shortly afterwards hear the sound of an Artouste engine whining into life. It seems to be idling for a long time without the rotors starting and then it is abruptly turned off.

Obviously there has been a start-up snag. The door next door is slammed so hard the whole building shudders and there is the thudding of a flak vest being thrown down and a stream of invective. I roll out of bed and, hopping into a pair of shorts, put my head round the door and ask what the problem is.

"I've just burned a fucking blade!" he answers, and I suck my breath sympathetically and withdraw diplomatically.

No charges follow, of course, but neither do they for the odd miscreant in the future, so the idea of finding out first-hand the problems in the bush has some benefits.

A few days later, Griff and I have just swapped roles when the Lynx crew changeover takes place and Starry Stevens arrives. He is an ex-navigator who retrained as a pilot and we haven't seen each other for some time. Lunch has just started and I am a firm believer in getting food in at the earliest opportunity as the chances of missing it altogether are otherwise very high. We arrange to have a chinwag later when he has stowed his kit.

I am about three forkfuls through my meal when the siren goes. I grab the steak and two slices of bread and take the sandwich with me to the briefing. An OP on the border is being mortared and fired on and the Lynx is to get there as soon as possible, followed by the fireforce. We are about halfway there when we hear Starry's part of his exchange with the callsign on the ground. Shortly after that it is apparent that he is putting in a sneb strike. We are now hearing the ground callsign intermittently as we come into range and he is putting in a second strike. They call and ask if he has hit the target.

"Standby. I've been hit."

Griff waits for about fifteen seconds and then calls and asks if he is OK. The delay is to give him a break to sort any problem out, the last thing you need is people calling you on the radio when there are things going wrong.

The reply is chilling, "Negative, I am on fire."

There is another break and then Griff calls again, "Echo Four, how's it going? Are you going to be all right?"

I can hear the absolutely calm and matter-of-fact delivery to this day, "Negative, negative, I am going to crash."

Griffiths calls several more times but there is no reply until the ground callsign comes up and tells us there was a lot of firing, the Lynx disappeared from their sight and there was a huge explosion.

We spend the rest of the afternoon, reinforced by the Grand Reef fireforce and now protected by a Hunter presence, trying to locate the wreckage. It is a pity the Hunters weren't used in the first place; it transpires that the enemy had deliberately initiated the incident to lure an aircraft into an ambush. The Lynxes have no front guns to cover their dive when delivering rockets or frantans and are very vulnerable to anyone brave enough to stand and shoot at them. None of the helicopters gets a shot fired at it during the search, the perpetrators are long gone, but now it is too late we have a pair of Hunters to escort us. It is eventually one of the Hunter drivers, Chris Abrams, who sees a gash in the bush from his high perch and directs us to the crash site. We have crossed over it a couple of times, but from our low height have not picked it up. One of the choppers lands, I think it is Mike Litson, and they recover Starry's remains. We spend the rest of the afternoon ferrying in troops to guard the wreck site overnight prior to demolition in the morning.

We are picking up scratch sticks hastily made up of cooks, bottle washers and all, from anywhere, and I take in the last stick of the day. I cannot find a spot to set down and settle into a low hover a few feet above the ground and tell the gunner to order them to jump out. In an assault landing the RLI are normally out before the aircraft has come to this low height and speed, but in all fairness to these guys they are not used to doing this. All the same I am mightily pissed off when I am called back a few minutes later to casevac one of them who has injured his leg jumping out.

It has been a long, sweaty and miserable afternoon, and after letting the blades come to a stop I look in the back of the chopper. Our casualty looks perfectly OK to me, and I sarcastically enquire whether he wants me to call an ambulance, or shall we piggyback him to the sickbay? He says that an ambulance will not be necessary but perhaps somebody could help him out to the ground and maybe he could lean on them down to the sickbay. My mouth drops and unfortunately the ground doesn't open to cover my embarrassment. This character has not one but two tin legs, blown off in a mine incident. He has refused a desk job in Salisbury and insists on doing his call-ups on bush operations, where, of course, one of the things he can't successfully do is jump out of helicopters – the short hop out he made over the way has pushed both his stumps into the tin legs. I apologise profusely, call for transport and stumble off to the bar. What a day!

Griffiths returns to Salisbury, and I resume leading the fireforce. We are repositioned at Grand Reef, Umtali, and are visited again by the boss; this time he has Norman Walsh, director of ops, and Mick McClaren, the Air Force commander, who are staying for a few days. Griff elects to fly a G-Car again, Yellow 6, and McClaren flies a few sorties with Mike Delport, Delta 4, in the Lynx. Along with our operational callsigns, we all have personal monikers that generally reflect where you stand in the hierarchy of the squadron and the air force – thus Griff is Alpha 7, head honcho of 7 Squadron, and McClaren is Alpha Zero, the MMWC, main munna what counts.

We have been to a couple of lemons and are at a scene on

the side of a kopje that looks as though it is about to become
another. We are just considering wrapping it up, when in the
funny way these things sometimes occur a stick makes contact
and the game starts. An assault stick of troops gets held up by
some terrs in a group of rocks and thick bush. We work it over
with the twenty mill, but I want some frantan on it before the
troops advance to clear the area. I call Mike in the Lynx, who
has the commander with him, and confirm the target. Because
the Lynx do not have front guns to cover their attack and are
very vulnerable to ground fire, we have devised a routine
where as they turn in live we will strafe the target area with the
cannon, ceasing fire as the Lynx comes peripherally into the
sight. This of course breaks all the 'safety' rules of weapons use,
but headquarters are primarily worried about the profligate
use of ammunition. There is an air staff instruction directing
us to use .303 to give covering fire if we feel it necessary, but
not twenty mill. They have no idea of the relative merits of the
two calibres in thick bush conditions, and the instruction is
widely ignored.

"K-Car, this is Delta 4, confirm you will give me covering
fire?"

"Delta 4, K-Car. Affirmative. Call 'in live'."

"K-Car, this is Yellow 6."

"Yellow 6 standby. I'll call you after the strike."

"Negative K-Car, this is Yellow 6, Alpha 7. Are you aware of
the order not to use the cannon?"

"Yellow 6 standby. After the strike."

"Negative Negative. K-Car you will not – repeat not – give
covering fire. Acknowledge".

"Alpha 7 Roger. Out to you. Delta 4 do you copy?"

"K-Car Delta 4 affirmative. No problem. Turning live."

We watch the strike go in, and pass the correction for the
second fran attack.

"Delta 4, K-Car, good. Restrike please. Add ten. Right five."

"Plus ten. Right five. Covering fire this time please".

Before I can reply, "This is Alpha 7, there will be no covering fire."

Unbeknown to us, the commander has thoroughly enjoyed participating in this live strike, but as the Lynx is climbing away, he asks what all the popping and cracking noises were. Delport laconically informs him that it was the enemy shooting at them and they have been hit a couple of times in the wing. This changes the commander's viewpoint on the merits of covering fire.

I'm trying to run this show, and still can't get a word in edgeways.

"Alpha 7, this is Alpha Zero. They will – repeat will – give covering fire. K-Car, do you copy?"

"K-Car affirmative. Delta 4 call 'in live'."

The second fran is a DH.

That seems to have resolved the mutual fire argument, and immediately on returning to Grand Reef, McClaren sends a signal throughout the force authorising this arrangement until the Lynx are modified with front guns.

The man is a prodigious party animal and a hooley is gathering momentum in the bar. I have an early flight in the morning and make my excuses about eleven o' clock to turn in and get some sleep. Norman Walsh – no slouch himself at revelling – follows me outside. He explains that McClaren is really fired up about the day's contact, gets little chance to socialise with his troops and it would be good to indulge him for a couple of beers.

Who is going to argue about a couple of beers? They are good drinking company anyway.

At some stage, we start convivial toasts of Castle lager to just about anything anybody can think of, and then in that peculiar way that time seems to have of telescoping we are all standing on the sandbags outside the mess toasting the arrival of the new day's sunrise. McClaren turns to me and says he thought I had a first light sortie. I laugh, and then realise he's serious.

"Well, get airborne then."

I balance my beer on the parapet and walk to the aircraft and get airborne. If there had been an accident, there would have been a very interesting board of enquiry – ordered to put down a beer and fly by the big boss. By the time we return, they have moved on and thankfully we have a quiet day so I can catch some zzz's.

CHAPTER SIX

Doris

Doris is my Old English sheepdog. He picked me out for special treatment, gambolling and sprawling over the length of a room to deliberately crap on my foot when I went to see the litter, the first of that breed born in Rhodesia. He's been flying since he was eight weeks old, and has more hours in helicopters than most of the air force. However, as I keep telling him, no one in the old dogs' home will ever believe him. He thinks I'm his mother, and there is obviously some Oedipus problem judging by the uncommon interest he shows in my leg on the odd occasions I get to shark in on one of the farmers' daughters or other odd bits of stray that turn up in the bush sometimes.

He travels everywhere with me. Initially I used to zip him up in a holdall with just his head sticking out, but now his chopper drills are immaculate. He loves flying, but has learned that when the siren goes for a fireforce callout he's not invited and doesn't even bother to come to the helipad, although he's invariably there to meet me when I land, and dutifully sits outside the rotor disc until the blades stop, to the delight of the troops.

There are other dogs around in the bush. Benji – or, more correctly, Sergeant Benji – has been a camp follower since Centenary days. He is mustered on strength, and earns his rations and the odd bonus for 'service above and beyond' by despatching rats and snakes around the gun pits and bunkers wherever he is posted. I think it is 2 Commando who have a dog that has been fitted with a harness and completed a parachute jump, and Ken Blain acquires a Red Setter, which also comes to the bush. Due to having been all over the country, however, Doris is a freer spirit, and more widely known these days, not least because he is a unique and quite astonishing sight on first meeting. He is a huge dog, and having no tail at one end and covered eyes at the other earns him the memorable description of being 'a two-way dog' by one of the goffals in a protection company.

There has been the odd problem. Some mining company executives were delayed for several hours until the fireforce returned, as nobody had the balls to drag the hairy apparition out of their aircraft, where he had settled in to the air conditioning for an afternoon siesta. If they had waved a stick of biltong, he'd have followed them to Bulawayo.

At Buffalo Range, Chiredzi, there is a daily Air Rhodesia flight and the aircraft stays for an hour or two before returning to Salisbury. Most of the airline's pilots do voluntary call-ups with the air force, and the girls are pretty good about bringing down mail and the odd goodies, so if we are not flying we generally wander over for tea and biccies whilst they are on the ground. If we are flying, Doris wanders over for his elevenses on his own.

We are just returning from a lemon one day as the Viscount is taking off. Ops call me and ask me to contact the Viscount captain direct. I call for a formation fuel check and switch frequencies, thinking that he has probably just been shot at and we can be overhead the scene in about three minutes. The captain is Robin Hood and he tells me not to worry about my dog, which up to that moment I hadn't. It transpires that he'd stretched out under some seats at the back of the aircraft and was only discovered after they were airborne. They are going to take him to Salisbury, he'll spend the night with one of the girls and they'll bring him down on the service tomorrow. He's started organising his own night stops! I'm jealous; I wouldn't mind a night with Mary-Ann either.

In general he gets on pretty well with the troops. On arriving at an FAF he does a quick recce and locates the kitchen first and the radio room next – the radio room generally being air conditioned. Third on his list is the bar – he knows if he hangs around there long enough I'll eventually turn up. He amazes everybody at Darwin one evening. The fireforce is out late and the bar is already open. He always hears the helicopters long before we've even made our joining call, and trots off to the pad to meet me. This time, however, the choppers are on finals and he is still stretched out on the deck. The troops try to throw him out and down to the pad, but he's having none of it and settles back down with his crisps. He's right, the K-Car isn't with the rest of them – apparently he can actually distinguish between the respective aircraft noises.

For some reason a lot of the techs and guards enjoy washing him when they're not working. I've never really understood engineers' preoccupations; maybe they are just compulsive about keeping things clean. They have a full-time job on their hands; he normally very quickly finds some mud to roll in. They are not so keen on his enthusiastic joining of their volleyball games but, as it is 'bush rules' and his indiscriminate chasing after the ball hampers both sides equally, he is accepted as a local hazard.

His chopper enplaning and deplaning drills take a while to hone. Not long after he outgrows his bag and is trusted to stay lying on the cabin floor, I have to fly from Vic Falls to Fort Victoria, which is right on the extreme range of the helicopter and takes about three and a half hours. As I taxi in, Doris is out of the aircraft before it stops. He makes directly for an angle-iron post next to the refuelling point and gets a leg in the air fast. It takes several minutes to cool the engine down and the blades stopped, but when they are he is still at it. There is a lake of ginormous proportions around the post, and he is desperately hopping around trying to keep his other three paws dry. If he'd let that loose in the aircraft we'd have been drowned. He doesn't make that mistake again and learns to go before we take off.

Some years later, when I am sailing on Lake Kariba, I notice him eyeing the mast thoughtfully, and remembering the capacity of his bladder quickly rig up a sling and use the boom as a derrick to hoist him into the water – there's no fear of flat dogs, he'll poison them.

We arrive at Mtoko and are treated to a live Tom and Jerry cartoon. Doris debusses and starts on his tour of inspection. One of the camp cats has recently had a litter and they are all out sunning themselves. Unfortunately, she is several yards away from them when an image from her worst nightmare comes prancing around the corner of the ops room and straight through the litter, which he doesn't even actually notice. Instinct takes over; there's spitting and snarling and she launches herself forwards to give him a good solid wallop on the nose, claws fully extended. The kittens wake up fast and disappear; there is a mighty roar from Doris, half pain and half rage. Apart from the odd paw being trodden on, he has never been hurt in his life. The cat realises that maybe she has acted a bit hastily and streaks away towards the mess hall at warp factor five with Doris about ten yards in line astern and accelerating fast. It is lunch time and perhaps she knows that, for him, the mess hall is off limits. As she gets inside, the concrete floor has a damp sheen on it and she can't get a grip. The legs are going like aircraft propellers, but she is hardly making any forward progress as the horizontal abominable snowman crashes through the door in hot pursuit. He has the red rage and has forgotten about the mess hall being out of bounds; the cat is going to die. He hits the greasy floor and is leaned over too far, loses his footing and momentum slides him into a collision with the cat. There is a scrabbling of paws never seen outside of a cartoon; the cat has hit the siren button and there is a high-pitched two-tone wailing which is accompanied by a continuous guttural growling from Doris. She's up first and off down the room with legs rotating at about 2000rpm and forward speed about six inches an hour, but Doris is, surprisingly, quickly back in the saddle and only a – bleeding – nose behind. He seems to have trained for the wet going better and is definitely gaining ground. People eating their lunch are in suspended animation, forkfuls of spaghetti poised halfway towards mouths.

Momma cat makes a lifesaving decision and leaps sideways, crashes over a table scattering ketchup, glasses, plates of bolognese and the rest, and hits the wall. The laws of gravity are suspended and somehow she sticks there. She has instinctively exploited one of the primary rules of combat – know your enemy's weaknesses. Doris is not equipped for a high-speed turning chase; he has no tail to balance out sudden changes of direction, and his fringe isn't conducive to pinpoint targeting. Not quite as bad as a super tanker, but it takes him a while to stop, reorganise himself, get turned around and relocate the cat.

Newton, however, has got fed up with the cat wasting her chance. The laws of gravity resume and the cat falls off the wall, knocks whatever was left on the table onto the floor and starts the high-speed moonwalk back towards the entrance. She gets there marginally ahead, which gives her a good start on the grass. She's at the top of the only tree in the vicinity in milliseconds. Doris gets up to about ten feet before he remembers he is a dog and crashes back to the ground like a sack of potatoes.

Subsequently, the cat becomes a nervous wreck. The kittens have reached that difficult age where they do the exact opposite of whatever they're told. They actually enjoy Doris, and he is quite happy for them to clamber all over him. Momma cat is frantic and keeps trying to call them away, but she is fully aware that Doris wants to discuss the nose business in more detail and keeps a respectful distance. It is several days before an uneasy truce develops and they come to some animal agreement that face will be saved all round if they ignore each other and go about their own business.

He has the dubious distinction of being one of the few dogs, if not the only one, to have been in aerial combat. As I said, they'll never believe his stories at the rest kennels. He doesn't come out of it well. We've spent a lot of time on fireforce duty with 3 Commando – nicknamed 'The Lovers', and he has obviously decided he is a lover not a fighter.

We are at Rutenga as a singleton helicopter on liaison duties with the army unit there. There is no war going on in this area at the moment – oh yeah – and the flying is 'routine'. What this really means is that our meagre resources are being penny-packeted around the country. The fireforces would be far more effective with more aircraft, and these detachments invariably turn into major dramas where you are involved in trying to control inexperienced troops engaged in a major punch-up with a new group of bad boys who are fresh, keen, rearmed and resupplied and have infiltrated the area whilst the SF have had their eye off the ball.

I have to take some signallers to the top of a big brick to repair a rebro station. Their task will take a couple of hours and I plan our day out so that I can wait at a girlfriend's nearby ranch, maintaining a listening watch on the radio. Alan Shields is my gunner, and Doris comes along for the ride. We drop the guys, have a very civilised lunch and siesta – or I do, Alan amuses himself polishing the gearbox or whatever – and eventually we go and uplift the team off the mountain.

It is late afternoon and we are cruising home pretty soporifically. About fifteen minutes out the day starts to go wrong.

The major problem from the air on arrival at a scene is determining if the gooks are there or not. We do not have the resources for keeping aircraft on station for long periods, and the fireforces quite often have other dramas to go to if things do not develop quickly at a callout. Once the aircraft are overhead, if the gooks are in cover they can make two big mistakes. Unless they move, it is extremely difficult to see them. But the biggest mistake of all is for them to open fire first, for then we know they are there. Our problem is not eliminating them, that is relatively straightforward once we are in contact. The problem is always locating them, and bringing them to contact.

There is a massive crash of rounds going through the cockpit and hitting the aircraft. We have flown over a base camp at about a thousand feet and presumably they thought an attack was imminent. It wasn't, but it certainly is now.

There is pandemonium in the aircraft. These are signallers, not combat troops, and they are just discovering that there is very little natural cover in a helicopter. Alan is cocking the twin brownings. I am turning hard left to get the guns to bear, and calling for the fireforce, which by good fortune is close by returning from a lemon, fat on fuel, fully armed and chomping at the bit. We are also in a fast descent as Doris has tried to jump on my lap. We have coincidentally solved the 'pulling excess power syndrome': with a hundred pounds of petrified dog sprawled across your left arm it is impossible to keep straight and level power, never mind any extra.

Alan opens up with the brownings, producing a tremendous banging and clattering which is really getting Doris' attention.

He starts making for my lap in a big way. I wasn't expecting to bat so I am not wearing a box and the left paw in the testicles produces enough incentive for my collective arm to throw him off. The collector bag on the gun has fallen off and hot ejected cartridge cases are flying around the cabin. One catches Doris in the ear and he changes tack, sees a small gap between the two signallers cowering on the front bench seat and goes for a fast climb across their shoulders and through to the very nose of the cockpit. A hundred pounds of dog arriving in a rush at the very front of the aircraft causes a fairly significant centre of gravity change but, for anybody compiling manuals on the subject, it is easier to deal with than the same weight cavorting around on your lap.

We manage to contain this three-ring circus until the fireforce arrives and takes over. There is a continual high-pitched whimpering; I can't make out if it's from Doris or the signallers.

When we land at Rutenga, Doris makes a reappearance, scrabbles frantically back over the two poor sods in the front and hits the ground running before we have come to a stop. I make a mental note to have a word with him about his deplaning drills but we have to refuel and rearm and get back to the fight, so leave him to it. The signallers are marginally slower, but only by a smidgen.

Amazingly we get a good result: eighteen out of twenty! The fireforce decide to stay for the night. Much beer is drunk and war stories tidied up. The only injuries on our side are bruising and claw marks on the cheeks of the two kids mauled by the demented dog. Doris eventually reappears in the bar. I tell him he's a disgrace, and in any case, nobody will believe him at Kozy Kennels, but he has that superior 'who is ever going to know the real truth' look and has obviously adjusted the details of his version of the battle and his part in it. The siggies are definitely going to have to modify their stories; who on earth is ever going to believe how they got their war wounds?

★

Although most of it is to come in the future, all in all, my nuts take quite a battering in the service of Rhodesia.

After an accident in an overweight Alouette, I need to be checked out by the squadron commander on landing and taking off at max all-up weight. Griffiths decides there is no point in getting one of the helicopters reconfigured with dual controls; this is a rubber stamp exercise, and with the aircraft loaded up with concrete blocks to max weight as stated in the manual, we are about half a ton under the weight we operate at in the bush normally. Poor old Mufti Upton is the tech.

We waffle around the flying area in Seke for a while and I eventually arrive in a confined area without hitting anything. Griffiths is sitting in the middle, and it is natural for him to be looking out to the left. I always fly with the sliding window open. I've just lifted into the hover when a wasp flies in the window, lands on the bridge of my nose and establishes territorial rights by stinging me. Griff hears me cry out, looks around and sees the wasp and promptly smacks me between the lamps. I now can't see a thing but am very aware of Mufti babbling over the intercom as the hover goes unstable. The bloody wasp drops into my lap. Now my eyes really start watering as Griff, who apparently really doesn't like wasps – I mean really, really doesn't like them – gives it another thundering smack, flattening both it and my nuts against the armoured seat.

Somehow, we wobble out of the confined area without making it too much larger chopping off odd branches, and I get to practise some actual limited panel instrument flying on the way back. It is very limited for several minutes as I can hardly see a thing. Mufti, who has been shot down a couple of times in the previous couple of weeks and is teetering on the edge of a nervous breakdown, has seen nothing of the wasp part of the incident and cannot make out why the pilot with his hands on the controls is crying his eyes out, and the squadron commander is duffing him up.

On landing we agree I've passed, Mike goes twitching and jibbering off to the sergeants' mess, and I take a long look at Doris and wonder how I can get into that licking position that dogs have mastered.

The accident that spawned the check flight comes with Butch Graydon as I am trying to land a very heavy aircraft on top of a hill. It is very hot, there is no wind and I make two wrong decisions – the first being to attempt the landing, and the second in attempting to climb away when the hover goes wrong in the tight LZ. There didn't seem to be a flat enough area to set down, but even so that would have been the better option. The Alouette does pretty well in its new capacity of lumberjacking and chops down fourteen trees before rolling over, shedding bits outwards. As such, the occupants come out of it OK as most of the energy has been absorbed, and the only injury is to Butch, who has a minor cut on his thigh.

The Board of Enquiry should be fairly straightforward; it is my fault. At the initial interview, I make the statement that I misjudged the approach and mishandled the controls. That should be that, smack on the wrist, don't do it again, but Grimshag is the president of the board and has decided to make a full production of it. One good thing comes immediately: every scrap of paperwork on the squadron, including my logbook that I have been trying to get signed for months, is brought up to date and signed, probably before the cooling metal has stopped creaking.

It becomes blatantly obvious that Grimshag is trying to nail me to the mast, and we explore a variety of scenarios, all subtly trying to show that I have been criminally negligent in some way rather than having made errors of judgement and skill. He realises he has gone too far when he calls George Wrigley in to give evidence under oath as an 'expert witness'. One of the board members and George both remark that the questions are becoming very leading, but he has to continue giving evidence and Grimshag is becoming very frustrated. His answers are not going in the right direction and are broadly in my favour, due to the conditions we are operating in and the nuances of helicopter aerodynamics that are not fully understood.

The president eventually ends up calling a halt to the proceedings and states:

"Well, this is going nowhere. Thanks a lot, George, but you can go, and we'll not be using this evidence."

There is some discussion about whether that can be done once a witness has been called, but Graham announces that as president, he can do what he likes. So far, I have said very little during these proceedings, but now pipe up to invoke my right to cross-examine any witness called, and I want to question George; I like his evidence.

"Well, we can call him back at some point in the future."

"No need, sir."

"Why not?"

"I'm just going to ask him exactly the same questions as you have, so we can just read his evidence into the proceedings as it stands."

There is a pregnant silence.

"We can't do that. The answers might be different."

The silence drags. "They had better not be, sir, they were given under oath."

George and Jerry Grindley, the engineering officer on the board, quietly chuckle, Grimshag is furious, calls an end to the day's proceedings, and further exchanges in the enquiry between him and me are very frosty.

They weigh all the extra kit – toolbags, armour plate, extra ammunition, etc etc etc – that we routinely carry in the aircraft and discover we are actually accepting empty weights of the aircraft that are several hundred pounds over the Form 700 entry, so the aircraft was well overweight. I am pleased that the official finding is very lenient; it is a very minor slap and the point is made that there must be latitude made to take consideration of the way we are being asked to operate. Of course, part of the minor 'slap' leads to the check flight where my nuts get a major slap – maybe Harold Griffiths is a friend of Grimshag, and has been asked to do it? Should have accepted my original statement.

I have a drink with George and thank him for his evidence. He says it was basically the truth, it was obvious there was a crucifixion in progress and he had crossed swords with Grimshag earlier in their careers, so it wasn't a problem.

There is an interesting postscript. I have been grounded during the board and am in fact reinstated before it is completed – the South Africans have been forced to withdraw their seconded pilots. I get a call in the Prospectors Bar from the boss – he knows where to find me – to put my beer down and get out to the squadron, I'm back on flying status, collect my medical clearance – examination not necessary – on the way, and fly down to Chiredzi to pick up a South African K-Car and reconstitute a fireforce as they can get people fitted in to replace the Slopes. I call in at the medical centre, collect my chit, and stop for afternoon tea in the garden. Paddy Morgan, a Canberra navigator, is there; he has had a lucky escape when a piece of shrapnel came into the aircraft and hit his chest on a low-level bombing run – he was wearing a flak vest. Also present are the medical officer and a couple of nursing staff, including

Denise, the wife of Ian Harvey, currently in headquarters but a helicopter pilot of renown. I am slightly perplexed by a remark she makes about my dealings with Graham Cronshaw, the board president – only he and I were present at the particular incident she mentions – but think little more of it. It transpires that they have been having an affair for years, and Norman Walsh, when commander, summarily sacks him as a group captain when he admits to the unforgivable sin of consorting with a junior's wife.

CHAPTER SEVEN

Doctor Knight

Without doubt, the most important and satisfying tasks of helicopter flying during the bush war were those of hot-extracting our special forces troops when they were in trouble on external operations, and casualty evacuation.

The ability to move seriously wounded people straight from the place of trauma to expert medical care is one of the great advantages of having rotary wing assets. The knowledge that there is an extraction team on standby if you get into serious trouble is the best of morale boosters to small teams on deep penetration missions far across the border.

Conventional military thinking normally dictates safety in numbers. Special forces' thinking tends towards minimising numbers as far as possible. Chris Schulenberg, the master of long-range reconnaissance, having re-joined the army as a Selous Scout after being awarded the Silver Cross whilst with C Squadron, SAS, brought this concept to its ultimate state by constituting two-man recce teams. He had experimented with one man callsigns, but accepted that it was beneficial to have an African as part of the team, to interpret observed rural behaviour, and on occasion to conduct ultra-close-in reconnaissance. In the bush war this meant snivelling into the enemy camps, sitting around their cooking fires and joining in the bullshit. The problem with small numbers is that if you are compromised and the enemy makes contact with you, you cannot normally tough it out in a firefight but have to run, or at least withdraw to an area where it is possible to be lifted by a helicopter. Schulie became the first, and one of only three, to be awarded the Grand Cross Valour. In fact, only two of these were in fact presented; the third was never gazetted as the recipient, another highly decorated Scout, Edward Piringondo, was killed, and the Rhodesians, with their extraordinary attitude to medals, withdrew the award.

The Rhodesian army's standard fighting formations were built up around sticks of four, normally constituted of a radio-equipped commander with rifle, two riflemen and a MAG gunner. This had been dictated by the load-carrying limitations of the Alouette helicopter. Both in weight and volume, four battle-equipped soldiers was the optimum load we could carry with any useful fuel load. Events sometimes dictated that this was exceeded – I hauled eight SAS troops out on a hot-extraction on one occasion, and in a relocation exercise when Caborra Bassa dam was filling up, Ian Harvey pulled over twenty villagers out in one lift, but they must have been pretty scrawny just to have fitted in volume-wise.

Throughout 1976, the eastern border was becoming more and more the principal area of operations. The country was generally densely wooded rugged mountains. In October, we are at Chipinga, one of the pleasanter FAFs to be at socially, as the airfield is practically in the town and the civilian population is very hospitable. The main produce hereabouts is coffee, which is very good. This combines with the local knicker elastic, which seems to be prone to regular failure, and leads to a lot of people sitting contentedly sipping their first brew of the day. However, from an operational point of view, locating and jousting with the gooks is a nightmare.

★

Aside from the large numbers of terrorists being infiltrated through the area to operate deeper inside Rhodesia, there are frequent hit and run raids on isolated farms at night, the terrorists returning to camps located over the border in Mocambique, protected by Frelimo troops.

In April 1974, the armed forces of Portugal staged a successful coup in Lisbon and General Spinola became the new president. By the end of July that year, plans were in hand to grant independence to Portugal's African provinces, Angola, Portuguese Guinea and Mocambique, by June 1975. The largely conscript army serving in Portuguese Africa decided that their main objective was to stay alive long enough to be repatriated to Portugal, and effectively withdrew to their barracks. By October 1974, Frelimo had become the de facto government of Mocambique and quickly found out the harsh realities of running a vast country, particularly as they were not themselves expecting to be in this position for a number of years. ZANLA at this time were also in a state of disarray, with lots of infighting and dissension following the assassination of Herbert Chitepo.

The Selous Scouts' aggressive and innovative commander, Lieutenant-Colonel Ron Reid-Daly had proposed a plan to establish themselves over the border as pseudo terrorists where they would be in a position to monitor and disrupt any future building of transit and base camps by ZANLA. This plan was turned down flatly, the powers directing the war believing, somewhat incongruously, that this would alienate Frelimo, who they incredibly thought wanted peace with Rhodesia and the continuing utilisation of their ports for Rhodesian trade.

Like all terrorist organisations, ZANLA has made suitable use of a short 'ceasefire' to retrain and reorganise its troops and establish safe 'firm' bases inside Mocambique that can be resupplied by road and rail from the ports of Beira and

Maputo, before reneging on the agreement at a time suited to themselves.

With Samora Machel officially closing his country's border with Rhodesia, our high command has effectively allowed the enemy to outflank us and provided us with the serious problem of several thousand kilometres of hostile border to police, which, aside from anything else, means that the territorial army has been forced into committing to longer call-ups with knock-on effects on the country's morale and economy.

A farm has been attacked just before dawn in a remote area about fifteen clicks on our side of the border. The farmer and his wife have returned fire and driven the attackers off, and by chance there was a tracker team at a police post in the vicinity who are already on tracks heading through the forest towards the border. We have a G-Car but no troops available, the rest of the fireforce having gone up to Umtali to support some operation and ending staying overnight, so I get airborne with the territorial army major and Brian Booth as the gunner. Brian is one of the new gunners on the squadron, about eighteen years old and known as Basil Brush due to his uncanny resemblance to the popular ventriloquist's dummy.

We arrive overhead of the trackers, who can't be seen due to the dense pine forest they are working through. We establish their position by getting them to read us overhead and take their sitrep – they reckon they are close up on tracks of two and about half an hour behind. We brief them that we will fly ahead along the line of flight of the gooks which will hopefully slow them down, and that if they make contact to throw a white phos. We'll then shoot through the trees in the area ahead of them on the far side of the white smoke, which will keep the gooks from running too far ahead.

Every ten minutes or so, the tracker stick reads us back overhead so we are up to date with their progress and their sitreps indicate that they are closing on the two fleeing insurgents.

Finally there is a whispered, "We have two CTs visual."

"Well done." This team has performed really well and caught up with the gooks about two hours after starting. There is a pause of about a minute before they come back on the air.

"What shall we do?"

"How far away are they?"

"About twenty-five yards." The major and I look at each other a little perplexed.

"What are these guys doing? Do they know you are there?"

"They're resting. No, they have no idea we are here." That explains the whispering.

The army officer and I exchange puzzled looks again. What is going on here? With the fireforce we normally get informed after the initial contact has taken place.

"Is there some problem? Can you not get a clear shot at them?"

"Negative. I've got one in my sights now, and the other one is covered with the MAG."

Jesus, what are they waiting for?

"Is there some reason you can't open fire?"

"Negative. Can I open fire?"

Good God!

"For Christ's sake, shoot!"

We wait for a couple of minutes – the last thing you need in the middle of a punch-up is somebody calling you on the radio – and then ask how things are going.

A bit breathless now, "OK. OK. Contact is over, we've got two dead CTs, no casualties to us."

We congratulate the callsign; they really have done very well to catch up and make contact so quickly. We give them directions towards a logging track and tell them that we'll make arrangements for the police to pick them and the bodies up on that road, and that we'll see them later.

We don't in fact meet this stick until the following day, and then the reason for the delay in initiating the contact becomes apparent. The stick leader is an eighteen-year-old, and the other three are seventeen, all doing their national service. They have recently been schoolboys and, of course, have spent their lives learning that you don't gratuitously kill things, let alone people. Slightly deeper analysis starts you wondering as to the ready acceptance of an authorisation from a disembodied voice over the radio, but anyway, the aggression and tracking skill shown by these school kids has really impressed me.

Shortly after landing from the trackers' contact I am introduced to another territorial, this time an officer who is a doctor on call-up duties. It is his first time in the bush, and we have a chat about where to take casevacs, and the procedure for taking him with us to incidents.

His baptism of fire comes about two hours later. We are called to ops and briefed on a situation at the Zona border post. The border post on our side has been under attack since the morning and is under small arms, RPG and mortar fire. There is no reason to believe the position is going to be assaulted but they have taken two serious casualties, can we pull them out?

We establish that these guys are very definitely in a serious way and throw two stretchers in the aircraft along with the territorial doctor and one of his assistants and fly up to a position in safe ground where we can assess the situation directly.

One of the casualties is very definitely on his last legs. The afternoon is starting to slide away, and we need to get him out now. Although the post is still coming under sporadic fire, I reckon that we can use a long spur of trees to mask our approach with some nap-of-the-earth flying, run-in and drop off the doctor, medic and stretchers and return when they have the patients ready for uplift. The poor doctor looks as though he's in a state of shock himself, using the trees as cover. I start to accelerate towards the open stretch for our run to the border post's LZ. As we break cover there is a frenzied popping of automatic small arms interspersed with a louder banging, accompanied by the cracking of rounds coming nearer, the thudding of hits on the fuselage and then a massive crash. The tail wags viciously, bits of Plexiglas shower the cockpit and my head is whiplashed from side to side. I do a sort of pedal-turn come wingover come high-speed rearward flight back into cover. Despite the rounds hitting the cockpit, none of us has been injured, but one round has severed the pigtail of my radio lead close to where it joins the helmet.

Further inspection after landing reveals that we have taken a couple of 12.7 hits through the tail boom, which accounts for the severe wagging of the tail. Nothing vital has been hit, so we have a rethink and make a plan to do an approach from a different direction and get the casualties aboard straight away. We arrange for a counter-mortar barrage from our own forces to cover the landing. Having got airborne once again we make a concealed approach and the two casevacs are loaded onto the floor of the aircraft without the stretchers and we are able to extricate ourselves without taking any further hits.

As we are running out I am having to lean forward to clear a see-through patch on the windscreen, as it is being obscured by arterial blood spraying from one of the casualties.

I turn to look. The doctor and medic are working feverishly, assisted by Brian. One of the soldiers has a great lump of shrapnel sticking out of his chest, but the three of them are ignoring this and desperately trying to halt the bleeding from his thigh, which is the cause of the spray of bright red blood onto the canopy. The other chap is lying quietly and I think that there is no chance of him surviving; half of his head has been blown away and his brains appear to be leaking down the side of the remains of his face.

Unable to speak on the intercom, I shout to Brian to find out if the doctor wants us to go to Umtali hospital, but he settles for Chipinga which is where we leave both the casevacs and the medical team. By the time we have finished it is pitch black, so we close up for the night, get the paperwork out of the way, send a signal ordering a new helmet and christen the new trophy – my pigtail-less helmet – in the bar.

The army medic arrives later in the evening. The two casualties are both still alive and in the process of being transferred by fixed-wing to Salisbury. Also, the doctor sends his compliments, and would we care to join him for a drink in the army mess? I am, probably luckily, by this time on the outside of very many Castle lagers, and tell the medic that we would certainly enjoy a few toots with the doctor, but it would be better if he joined us. Also, we don't stand on such ceremony as issuing official invites in the bush.

"Well, sir, he was very worried that you'd be the moer-in with him after the a/d."

The bar falls silent. "A/d? What a/d?" It turns out that when we had first come under fire, the doctor decided to cock his weapon, an Uzi submachine gun. It's pretty hard to have an a/d, accidental discharge – which is almost always an n/d, negligent discharge – with an Uzi, as there are several safety features designed to preclude it. Anyway, the doc managed to overcome all the obstacles at the first try and then keep his finger on the trigger, emptying a full magazine of 9mm bullets. The hits in the cockpit, including the severing of my pigtail have been from outgoing fire not incoming. Had I known at the time I quite likely would have throttled him, but hours later it all seems quite funny, so we settle on a summary punishment of drinks all round and continue the party.

A Trojan courier aircraft arrives the following afternoon to take me to Salisbury. On arrival, I am ordered to present myself in best bib and tucker at headquarters to discuss why I had deliberately put valuable government property in harm's way.

I arrive at the appointed hour and, of course, am made to hang around outside the headmaster's study for the statutory period in order that I appreciate I am deep in the dwang. I listen carefully to a cost-benefit lecture on why helicopters should not be hazarded unnecessarily. This sort of discussion is invariably one-sided, it is an interview very definitely without coffee, and my only role in it is to give the group captain a good listening to, and eventually, suitably chastened, salute, about-turn and leave his office. Chastened? I am delighted, I can't believe I am getting two nights in Salisbury. I've brought my 'dog robbers' into town with me in a holdall left with Terry Emsley, so I'm getting a buckshee afternoon as well.

Before changing and whistling off for a liquid lunch, I go along to headquarters' ops room, thinking to look at some of the airstrike reports from other fireforces. A smart, charming and efficient RWS sergeant informs me that I can't enter the ops room as I'm not security-cleared, which is fair enough, and that I can't read the airstrike reports anyway as they are 'Top Secret'. Can't read them? I wrote a fair proportion of them, and surely one of the benefits of producing them is that we learn of errors or innovations of other pilots. She is unconvinced by this, and it takes the intervention of John Matthews, the ops officer, before I am allowed to enter the inner sanctum and read the files. By this time I've lost any enthusiasm and the pubs are open, so after glancing through a couple of pages I make my excuses and successfully escape from this Alice in Wonderland building whose occupants seem to be living in a different universe to the rest of us. The principal topic of discussion as I leave is the previous day's bridge school.

Slightly over a year later, I am in the Prospector Bar of the Monomatapa hotel putting in some serious marketing with a blonde air hostess. It is a popular bar with any SF in town and is always fairly full of a mixture of soldiers, airmen and police in various stages of inebriation. The army generally only knows the bush aircrew, and of these are most closely acquainted with the helicopter crews. Although we would know the officers, senior NCOs and some of the characters in the various commandos, many of the troopers are just self-loading cargo that we carry in the choppers. Two troopies come up and ask to buy me a beer. I am at a critical point of negotiations, so thank them but say I'm fine just now. They carry on, obviously much the worse for wear, one being visibly unsteady on his feet and the other slurring his speech, insisting that I have a beer.

I turn to face them, irritated rather than annoyed. I don't usually turn down free drinks, but I am planning on switching to wine in the jacuzzi just now and don't want to lose the momentum leading that way.

"Sir. You must have a drink with us, you saved our lives." The slurred speech isn't alcohol-induced. The guy has a slope on the right side of his head, where a metal plate has been inserted, and not much use in his left arm, but is otherwise alive – the chap I had last seen with his brains leaking onto the floor of the helicopter. The other chap has a tin leg.

We have very many beers. I want to take them over the road to hindquarters and reconstitute the cost-benefit analysis of helicopter employment, but nobody would understand, and we are enjoying the beer and being alive too much. The air hostess has to settle for washing herself.

As an aside, in a discussion with this chap on a later occasion, he casually tells me that he had 'died' whilst on the operating table. He continues with a tale of travelling along a tunnel of light, a feeling of peace, and of meeting his mother who was waiting for him at the end of the tunnel. She tells him that she is glad to see him, is waiting for him and looking forward to their meeting again but this isn't the time and he is to go back. I am thoroughly impressed with his story, particularly because he is so matter-of-fact about it. He isn't trying to impress anyone, and it is obvious he doesn't give a damn whether or not anybody believes him; it had happened. I don't believe he has the imagination to have made such a story up. And why would he? I hope he lives a long and happy life.

The subject of casevacs can be very contentious. To me, one of the interesting factors in the bollocking I received for that episode was that the concern was for the damage to, and possible loss of, the helicopter; no mention was made of the crew. The facility for helicopter evacuation is a great morale booster for troops in combat, and there is no doubt that the swift transferral of severely wounded men to good medical care saved very many lives in the Rhodesian conflict. Some of the gunners become very good at administering trauma first aid. Peter McCabe carries a comprehensive medical kit and has been personally responsible for saving several troopies' lives. However, there is a tendency to treat any injury or wound as life-threatening and deserving of an airborne response – particularly at night. At night, every snakebite is from a mamba. They invariably are not, even though I can understand the response. There is nothing to be gained in risking the loss of an aircraft and crew in a task that could as well have waited for daylight. I recall being called whilst leading a section of G-Cars through the Vumba Mountains towards dusk, and asked if we could lift a casualty off from a relay station on the top of a mountain. The other helicopters go into an orbit whilst we approach and land on a fairly tricky pinnacle as the light is failing fast. I am astounded when a soldier walks to the helicopter carrying a suitcase of all things and sits in the back. I am tempted to throw him off and take off again but, having got onto the LZ, decide to just to carry on with the task. As it happens he has chicken pox or something quite seriously, and the doctors at Umtali hospital are glad to get him there, but it was hardly worth the risk of a night landing in the mountains.

Casevacs often go hand in hand with that other contentious subject, medals. I am peripherally involved in an event where Gaps Newsman successfully carries out a night casevac under fire in the mountains. The grateful army unit concerned puts him up for a Bronze Cross. I read the paper that comes down to the squadron from the medals committee. It reads in part:

'This sort of action has become so commonplace for pilots from 7 Squadron that we do not feel we can continue to award the Bronze Cross for its recognition. However, do look at Air Lieutenant Newman's overall performance and he will be considered for an alternative award.'

To me, it is exactly this sort of nonsense that causes the disaffection surrounding awards. If that is what is required to earn a Bronze Cross then that is what it is. Not that that is the requirement until a few have been handed out, and then the criteria change. There is another aspect to the matter as well. Generally, these sorts of flights are taken in direct contravention of standing orders, and although when successful there are pats on the back all round and congratulations on the display of initiative, blah, blah, fishpaste, etc, if a disaster were to take place there would be the combined sounds of teeth being sucked and shoulders sloping to avoid any portion of blame attaching itself. Ken eventually receives a DMM. Tol Janeke, OC Op Repulse, sounds off one night and is of the opinion that those bloody people in headquarters should stop giving each other medals, and recognise what some of these young pilots are doing. As it is, most of the MFCs handed out would probably be DFCs in other air forces. As for Tol, I don't think he's ever forgiven me for an incident when a dead terrorist's body was required by Special Branch urgently in Salisbury for identification purposes – he was some sort of heavy. I pointed out that we needed all the helos at first light for an upcoming punch-up, and the only alternative was for him to fly the Trojan up with the floppie strapped in beside him. He says afterwards it was a surreal experience with the body gently rocking backwards and forwards in the red glow of the instruments, and he nearly has a seizure when a tremendous burp erupts into the drone of the Trog's engine, busy turning fuel into noise.

★

The Trojan itself is an amazing testimony to aerodynamics – it is one of the extraordinary acquisitions of the sanctions busting team, goodness only knows what they were thinking in the first place, and they manage to get ripped off by getting the version with the low-powered engine. Most of the Air Force has flown it – I think on the basis that if you operate one of them, you can probably fly anything. I have only ever flown in them twice, once being a most horrifying experience sitting in the back whilst Ed Potterton is teaching Ray Bolton to fire rockets. The attack profile involves closing the throttle, and you can almost hear the sigh of pleasure from the airframe as it is finally allowed to give up the battle to maintain lift and to do what it is eminently suitable for – hurtle towards the ground. The rockets go at what seems to me a very late stage in the dive and there is something like a 4G pull out, with me having visions of the high wing folding overhead.

But they are strong. We go in to pick up Ian Sheffield, in

the days before he became Christina, who force lands in trees in Mocambique at night. The main spar absorbs a lot of the forward energy and probably saves his head from being stoved in. After all that he goes and has a full sex change after the war, which presumably means having part of your brain removed as well as the wobbly bits fitted, so the main spar's intervention was redundant.

Ray Dawson, one of the RLI's doctors, told me once that if somebody was still alive an hour after they had been shot, they were not bleeding to death and were stabilised as far as warmth and fluids were concerned, the chances were that they would survive the night. I have an awful experience one night in the Honde valley, in the Inyanga Mountains. An RAR stick of eight has been banjoed and, having fought off the ambush, is left with three serious casevacs and two minor. There is a new moon, which technically means we are forbidden to fly. The weather is cloud and rain anyway, so the lack of a moon is fairly irrelevant – it is as black as a witch's tit. From Ruda airfield, which is the headquarters of the company involved, I speak with the stick leader and tell him that I will try and air taxi up a re-entrant to the gridref of his position. When I call for it, I want him to send an 'Icarus' parachute flare up to illuminate the area. Each member of the stick carries a flare, and they burn for over a minute. I impress on him that once he has sent the first up he is to keep the rest going in a continuous stream so that there is always light – not to wait until one dies out before firing another.

He understands, and we start a hover climb up the steep mountain side, the landing light illuminating the re-entrant I am using as a reference, and after requesting them, four flares go off in succession to provide an eerie light in the misty rain. We are going to hack this.

Suddenly, the sky above reverts to black. I lose all reference apart from the spot of landing light which was showing the stream bed, then the treetops, then the stream again. The tech screams out that the tail rotor is nearly in the water. I suddenly realise that with my disorientation the fuselage is now parallel with the stream, which means that we have something like a seventy-degree nose-up attitude and we are actually moving backwards downhill. I pull power to take us away from the mountainside, sort of pedal turned around so that the nose is pointing downhill – absolutely pitch black now as the light is shining out into the abyss of the valley. I pull the cyclic back to try and get level, praying that the tail rotor is clear of obstructions on the mountainside, and with the collective still up, climb rapidly up through the night. As I get above the level of the mountains I can make out the lights of Ruda, previously screened by the terrain, which give me some reference and sort things out so that we are flying straight and level in some sort of coherent manner. I have been aware of the callsign on the ground calling on the radio, and now have time to answer him. The poor bugger had sent the flare up and it hadn't ignited, hence the blackness. He'd got another off immediately, but as I look down and see a glow below us I realise we had already climbed past it before it had illuminated. He asks if we are going to come in again, and I reluctantly tell him there is no chance but I will be back at first light.

We get in in the very first lightening of the dawn, but sadly it is to lift out one body and the two serious GSWs; we go back later to lift the rest out.

The stick commander is a platoon warrant officer who has served with the RAR in Malaya in support of Britain's fight against a communist incursion. I am told afterwards that the soldier who died was wounded so badly he wouldn't have survived in any event, but it doesn't make anybody feel any better. We leave the survivors – all black, of course, in this war that is portrayed in the United Nations as a group of white racists fighting black freedom fighters – who are embarrassingly grateful that we had attempted the rescue and then come back for them – reorganising themselves to be redeployed on patrol, and ease back to Grand Reef feeling very, very sad.

CHAPTER EIGHT

Kanyemba

We are from Mount Darwin as part of a mini fireforce and positioned forward at Rusape. It is late afternoon. We have lazed about all day waiting for a 'scene' to develop, but the afternoon is dragging along and we will soon be packing up to go home for the night. A Dakota arrives overhead and does a couple of orbits of the airstrip, which is dirt and pretty short. I call them on the radio and find out that the pilot is Ian Rodwell – he doesn't have paratroops on board, but is qualifying a co-pilot for bush operations. He has come here to practise shortfield landings and then will spend a few days at Darwin to finish the conversion. We return to our various patches of shade and a desultory game of bridge. The Dak does a touch-and-go landing, there is a roar as the engines are brought to full power immediately and it leaps back into the air. After watching a couple of these circuits, everybody loses interest and, apart from the regular bursts of power application as the aircraft rolls after its short landings, the afternoon reverts to its soporific atmosphere.

The noise of the engines on final approach has become pure background, no more significant than the cicadas and the distant goat bells and calling of the young boys herding cattle, when there is a sudden increase in the roar, and a crashing, followed by a series of sharp cracks. We all leap up or start rolling for cover, looking to the runway, where the old transport is framed by pieces of exploding banana tree – in an attempt to set down on the very threshold of the runway they have brought it too low and it has run through some bananas on the approach. They climb away and we call on the radio. Having ascertained that they are OK, we tell them to have the beers waiting when we get back, signing off with the remark that it is an interesting technique and will certainly make it easier for the next crew to land.

The pilot being 'qualified' is a reservist, who is a very high-time ex air force instructor and Air Rhodesia captain, Patrick Forbes, who is now retired and runs a farm at Centenary. He hasn't flown for a number of years – hence the refamiliarisation – but there has been a recent increase in the call-up requirement, and just about anybody who can spell aeroplane is being inducted into the air force.

He is a great friend of Jerry Lynch, the other Dak pilot, and slips easily back into the life of a bush detachment, but has obviously got too used to packing for hotel night stops with an airline rather than a week at a forward airfield, as he has forgotten various items of personal kit.

There is a brief burst from the siren, and our mini-force gathers in the army ops room. There is a foot patrol on the edge of the Zambezi that is pinned down with heavy fire from across the border with Zambia – they have a serious casualty and need him uplifted as soon as possible.

Both the G-Car pilot and Lynx driver are pilots on call ups, but both are very experienced. Wing Commander Hofmeyer is one of the 7 Squadron originals, but has been in headquarters on non-flying duties for a number of years, and the Lynx pilot, Mike Saunders, is an ex commander of the Hunter squadron, renowned for embracing the 'fighter-pilot' ethos in its entirety, so with no hope of developing a career in the air force, who runs his own aerial crop-spraying business.

We devise a plan and set off for Kanyemba. We have asked for Hunter support and they RV with us about five minutes before we get to the target area. My plan for extracting the injured man will involve the Hunters striking the Zambian positions whilst I run the helicopters in from the west along the river. With the gunship on the left I can cover Hoffie on his vulnerable left flank as he lands and picks up the stretcher.

The Hunter leader, Rob MacGregor – who has only recently left our outfit where he was an excellent and understated flight commander and instructor – informs us they are under direct orders that they are not to strike over the border other than in the absolute dire strait of the case of saving Rhodesian life. This doesn't include the life that we've come to extricate apparently. I totally unreasonably lose my temper with Rob. He tells me to standby and I hear him calling Air HQ – because they are flying at thirty odd thousand feet they have direct VHF comms back to Salisbury – and requesting permission to strike to cover us, but the request is turned down. I tell them they may as well bugger off back to Thornhill as they seem to be on some sort of navigation exercise, and rehash a plan where Mike Saunders and I will go over the river and engage the bad guys whilst Hoffie does his pick-up. Rob comes back on the air and asks if he should get this authorised by Air HQ and I tell him no thanks. They of course have heard his half of the conversation with us and start badgering him to know what is going on. He plays his part well and tells them to stay off the air as we are in the process of carrying out the casevac.

Mike and I co-ordinate an attack where he frantans the enemy position from the east whilst we are running in at ultra-low-level from the west. As the frans explode on our left we pass right along the enemy position with the 20mm raking the whole area and then climb around behind him in a left-hand climbing turn which enables us to keep the gun firing continuously.

We carry on with our cannon and several restrikes of his 37mm sneb rockets. I have kept an eye on Hoffie whilst all this is going on and he has snuck in and landed for the casevac. He lifts a minute later and disappears round some high ground, calling clear of the area. We give the Zambians a final going over and clear the area ourselves, leaving the target burning fiercely.

The stretcher case is transferred to the Dakota at Kanyemba airfield, the base of the patrol we have just been assisting, who are very grateful for our help, and they set off for Salisbury. After some tea with the unit commander, we lift for Mount Darwin, but shortly after I split company with Hoffie and take a more southerly course, climbing up over the escarpment. My gunner is one of the new youngsters, SAC 'JJ' Jacobs, and he is obviously mystified where we are going but doesn't say anything. A few minutes after cresting the escarpment I reach a farm which we circle a couple of times. A young woman comes out with a child in her arms and another holding her skirt. She looks up and waves and I descend in a tight spiral and land on the lawn.

We are sitting on the verandah having our second afternoon tea of the day when there is a sudden and mighty roar of aero engines and the Dakota flashes overhead at low level. This is Pat Forbes' farm. I've decided to call in and get his toothbrush, pyjamas, teddy bear and whatever else he is missing and has been whining about since arriving at Darwin. The transport hurtles into a fighter-type wingover and practically stands on its wingtip as the pilots are taking great interest in this tea party Forbes' very attractive young wife is having with a helicopter crew. We lean back and wave, and after a few orbits they ease off, but on my arrival at Darwin much later he interrogates me at great length. Eventually he is satisfied that it was a mission of mercy – which I would have carried out for him, even had it been an ancient aunt I was collecting from – but he gets the hump again some days later when a parcel arrives clearly addressed to me in his wife's handwriting, containing some fresh paw-paws that I had remarked on, and a freshly baked cake. He refuses my offer of a slice – he doesn't like sharing, obviously, wives or cake.

Hoffie, Saunders and I concoct a suitably edited airstrike report, and agree that it is an appalling reflection on the way our operations are directed that we have to do so. Do characters in Salisbury really appreciate what is going on out here in the op area? A guy's life is ebbing away, and we have to lie to explain how we extricate him?

CHAPTER NINE

Madula Pan

It is axiomatic to talk of wars 'hotting up', or being vicious or whatever. If you are the person being shot at, any battle is hot enough for the time being. However, the incursions of terrorists started gathering momentum in 1975. It was also apparent that the gooks had started to acquire the techniques of aiming off to fire at the helicopters with small arms, and we were starting to take hits quite regularly. Requests from pilots in the bush to fit some protective armour plating were met with a response not dissimilar to that of the British air staff in World War I for requests to supply pilots with parachutes – "What's the matter with you?"

Because we only had the Alouette 3 at that time for all our helicopter work, there was a constant equation going on of weight of troops against fuel against distance etc. Obviously, the less the basic helicopter and crew equipment weighed, the more fuel and troops could be carried. The sticks of troops were standardised at four, by the army at least – it took the police a while longer to come into linev– and we more or less standardised the normal fuel weight to give us just about an hour and a quarter's flying time. Any extra weight in the form of armour protection would necessitate either dropping the fuel load, or using more power in any given phase of flight. At that time, the pilots sat in half-bucket seats that sort of protected the family jewels and dung funnel, but the air staff were actually – seriously – considering having these removed to save weight. The seats, that is. Most aircrew had made their own arrangements, with old flak vests wedged around them, metal plates stuck on the floor, and in the case of the gunners, tool bags placed under their seats.

Events started to lead, and once taking casualties from small arms fire in fireforce engagements became regular it was decided to issue helicopter crews with flak jackets. In little over a year's time, the helicopters would be fitted with massive armoured seats for the pilots, giving protection up and around the back and sides of the head, and eventually with an extended 'heart shield' to protect the left side of the body, where the seat had to be cut away in order to allow the pilot's left arm to operate the collective control. In the K-Car gunships the gunner and army commander were also given this protection. Surprisingly, or actually perhaps not, we always seemed to be able to force the power out of the machines – I can hear Geoff Dartnall, the squadron engineering officer, still groaning now!

Anyway, the first escalation in aircrew protection was to issue us all with flak jackets. The first few arrive on the squadron, and, interestingly, just about everybody who tries them on initially dons them back to front. They are in two pieces, a heavy front breastplate and a thinner more flexible back that Velcro together over the shoulders and at the waist. We are all obviously more worried about our backs, as that was the way they were all initially tried on. Actually, the reason may have been subtler than that, the body sub-consciously protecting itself from what it saw as the real potential threat: being stabbed in the back. You could always tell helicopter aircrew; they as often as not had cuts and bumps on the bridge of their noses and chins where the damn breast plates hit them getting them on and off, particularly in a scramble.

One is duly selected by the officer responsible for their procurement, and we all troop off to the range to watch a demonstration as to its effectiveness. The breastplate is set up on the sand of the twenty-five-yard range, and some bod with an FN fires at it. Off we go to inspect it, and there is a lot of holding of chins, tugging of ears and not too much cheering – the round had gone straight through!

In all fairness, later tests stop the AK round at the same distance, deflect the FN round at any angle other than head-on, and stop it head-on at thirty-five yards. Anyway, nobody turns down the offer of wearing them, and off we go to joust, clouting our noses putting them on and our chins taking them off.

★

On the morning of 12th January 1977, we are about to have another practical demonstration of locally produced new pieces of kit, 'rams' – radio-activated marker system – and the Alpha bomb.

In April 1974, a Canberra flown by Keith Goddard and Richard Airey engaged on a low-level bomb-run in Mocambique near Macombe crashed, killing both the crew. The aircraft had been dropping a bomb load of ninety-six 20lb fragmentation bombs. The Board of Inquiry arranged for film to be taken of these bombs being dropped from a Canberra. Seeing the chaotic behaviour of the bombs as they hit the slipstream, and some of the arming caps spinning off, thereby arming the bombs, directly under the aircraft, the board concluded that the most likely cause of the crash was that an armed bomb touched another and detonated just after weapons release, causing a chain reaction detonation of the full bomb load. Consequently, the Canberra was no longer employed in delivering anti-personnel bombs.

A project to design and produce a suitable anti-personnel

weapon was overseen by Wing-Commander PB Petter-Bowyer and Denzil Cochran. Probably the principal challenge in designing an effective AP weapon to be air-delivered is getting the detonation at a suitable height. The solution was brilliantly simple. They came up with a spherical bomb, which in fact was two spheres, one inside the other. Between the two spheres was a rubber compound filled with two-hundred-odd small, metal balls. As the bomb hit the ground the fusing started, the weapon bounced back into the air and was detonated a fraction of a second later at a height of about nine feet, spraying a lot of lethally bad news around at exactly the right height.

The weapons were about six inches in diameter, and a system was designed for the Canberra bomb bay whereby three hoppers could hold a hundred bombs each. These could be dropped in batches of fifty at a time, but generally they were normally deposited in full loads, which would cover an area of seventy-five yards wide by half a mile long, with the aircraft running in at 330 knots and 300 feet.

The 'rams' had been developed by the radio section at New Sarum. A close-in recce team would position two flares at a known bearing from a target, one closer than eight hundred metres, and the other between two and four kilometres. On the bomb-run, the Canberra would activate the system, a radio signal triggering the ignition of the flares, and the navigator, using the off-set technique, would use the first flare to command final course corrections, and the second to initiate bomb release.

Special Branch intelligence has indicated that there is a ZANLA transit camp some fifty miles south of the Rhodesian border. This gen is supported by signals intercepts and finally confirmed by photo-recce to be located at Madula Pan, situated just to the west of the railway line. Planning has been undertaken to strike this camp when it has a transient group of insurgents in residence for final resupply en-route to Rhodesia. Radio intelligence gives positive indication that the camp will be occupied by a large group of transients between the 10th and 12th of January 1977. A strike of three Canberras is arranged for the night of the 11th/12th bombing on rams flares positioned by a Selous Scouts recce team, and using alphas.

The task of the helicopter force is to take in a team of twelve Selous Scouts to assess the battle damage of the bombs, collect any intelligence material and possibly prisoners and count the casualties. The initial plan is to land the helicopters in the pan near the camp, and refuel them from an airdrop by a Dakota, whilst the Scouts are sweeping through the camp. Wiser counsel prevails, and this part of the plan is vetoed, a couple of extra helicopters are assigned to us so that each G-Car carries only two soldiers and enough fuel to complete the round trip. They will then be recalled when required for uplift of troops and any materials. At the same time we will also extract the recce team who have placed the flares for the Canberras to bomb on.

The strike force is to be three Canberras with a fourth aircraft bombed up and airborne in reserve. This fourth aircraft will also carry Captain Rob Warracker of the Selous Scouts, recently decorated with the Silver Cross of Rhodesia, as at high level he can establish VHF comms with the recce team – their batteries are low and we don't need any foul-ups with their position when the time comes for pick up. Only after much persuasion is it agreed that we can have a pair of Hunters lurking overhead, but despite repeated requests otherwise, they will be armed with SNEB rockets, not frantan. 1 Squadron are not keen on using frantan, as it is not a point-delivery weapon – they like to be able to deliver their weaponry onto specific targets. Frantan – short for 'frangible tank' is a locally produced type of napalm, and a firm favourite with fireforce operators, either army or air force, for getting the enemy's attention when he hasn't read the script properly and is fighting back instead of running away.

During the briefing there is an underlying atmosphere of "Why are you making so much fuss, you're only going in to count the bodies?" The census team are even less happy, of course; they are actually going onto the ground into a camp supposedly occupied by a large number of people who, if they hadn't for some reason been despatched, were going to be fairly crabby about having their night disturbed by several hundred noisy footballs hurtling through their bashas. The air effort is completed by the Dakota, which will be airborne with some fuel drums and boxed 20mm ammunition for the K-Cars rigged up for para-dropping in an emergency; Wing Commander Tol Janeke in a C185, who will coordinate the air effort and act as Telstar (radio relay); and the helicopters – two K-Cars and six G-Cars.

The planning staffs, both air and ground, are confident this is going to be an academic exercise to confirm the success of the alphas. The assault forces, both air and ground, are distinctly uncomfortable about the prospect of waltzing down fifty miles across the border, up close to the railway line. At least we've managed to get the plan modified so that we have an extra K-Car, and we all now have enough fuel to get back to our own side of the Mason-Dixon Line if necessary.

I am mates with Rob Warracker, who I'd originally met at Mkumbura on my first operational bush tour. I'd recently got involved in a horrifying drinking episode with him and Schulie at the Sahara bar in Salisbury whilst on R and R. The Sahara bar is above the Coq d'Or, the favourite haunt of the RLI, and generally a bit quieter. This was the first time I'd met Schulie, who was already a legend, having earned a Silver Cross with C Squadron, SAS, left the army, and then rejoined specifically to develop small-team long-range recces with the Selous Scouts.

He'd originally wanted to rejoin the squadron, but they were not flexible enough to accommodate his very original ideas on intelligence gathering, and in a way the Scouts were probably one of the few formal military units in the world that could integrate the ultimate lateral thinker. Also present at this drinking session, which was to celebrate Rob's recent award of the Silver Cross, was Padre Grant. Warracker is about my height, but much stockier. Schulie is huge. They started a face-slapping exercise, taking turns to clap each other in the chops to see who is going to buy the next round. Padre Grant and I watch in fascinated horror, silently worrying about who is going to be paying for the round after that.

Schulie and Sergeant Stephen Mpofu, who is the other member of the two-man recce team, are parachuted in from the Dakota on the night of the 10th and, having slowly moved in to carry out a close-in recce of the camp, are able to confirm the presence of a large number of insurgents and, not without some difficulty, succeed in positioning the target-marking flares at the positions pre-selected from air photos. We have, of course, had helicopters on hot-extraction duty to go and pull them out since they were dropped.

The reason the Can strike is going in several hours before dawn is that it is known the camp is vacated during the day specifically in case of attack. We are planning to pull up overhead at 'first shooting light', which is about half an hour after dawn. Ideally, we wanted the Cans to pass through on their bomb run within a minute before we get to the target – if the planners are worried about helicopter noise, five minutes before, but as close as possible before our arrival anyway. There are more mutterings about what the big deal is as "it is only to assess battle damage, it isn't a camp attack" and the plan stays for the Cans to go through long before us.

Everybody is convinced this is going to be a milk run.

Apart from the milkmen that is, and our vote doesn't seem to count for too much. Afterwards, I think this operation was paramount in getting the staff to change their thinking about how to achieve the best results in combined forces camp attacks. After all, why use thinking the subject through first when you can learn the hard way? This sort of multi-type strike should be governed by H-hour being worked backwards from the helicopters' arrival, and the other aircraft adjusting their ToTs accordingly, not the other way around. The jets have a lot of flexibility in loitering off target, the helos, with our low speeds and small excess power availability, can only adjust our timings minimally once we are launched. Because we are always flying around heavy and by definition are at high-density altitudes (i.e. hot and high), we are almost always at very high power settings. The first time I fly an Alouette after the war, I am at sea level in a light aircraft; I haul in a great chunk of collective to get airborne and rocket skyward like a champagne cork out of the bottle; it takes some time to realise that in normal flight conditions, there are other collective positions than either fully down or close to full power.

Towards last light on the 11th we prepare to depart Chiredzi. Doris, my Old English Sheepdog, comes and sits hopefully by the helicopter and wanders off towards the troopies' bar conveying his normal disdain when I tell him "Sorry old boy, not this time". We bed down at Malapati, where final checks are carried out and the aircraft readied for our before-first-light launch.

Our formation is to be two K-Cars, myself leading with Major Bert Sachse as the army commander and JB the gunner, Pete Simmonds in the second gunship trailing about a minute, and the six G-Cars, led by Chris Dickinson, trailing about five minutes behind him. There has been some comment about this straggled formation at the final briefing, but I'd explained that with the fairly limited loiter time of the G-Cars, Bert and I want to get a good look from overhead before having to direct them to a landing zone, and there is always the noise factor to consider. I think I have a feeling in my water!

Simmo is crewed only with a gunner, so has no weight problems with as much fuel and ammunition as they can stuff in. And I have my flexible attitude to rolling off overweight – Geoff Dartnall groaning again – on the basis that one of the most useless things in aviation is the fuel you left on the ground behind you – so we are pretty fat on fuel as well, even with Bert on board.

I personally have no trouble sleeping before these things, sling a mosquito net under the wing of the Dak and get in some zzz's, but I think most of the guys stay awake, drinking coffee, bullshitting and the rest. About an hour before dawn we are all up, kitted out and getting some coffee and odd bits out of rat packs down our necks, when from the south we hear a long deep rumbling – this is the Canberras waking up Madula Pan with 900 bouncing bombs. We still have a while to go before taking off.

There's a great tendency to do everything early; everybody's geared up like before a big rugby game, so we are all in our aircraft strapped in and waiting for about five minutes before time for engine start. On fireforce scrambles you just tumble into the aircraft, the techs generally already have the engine going, and you are engaging the rotors, checking in on the radio, strapping in and organising maps, weapons and the rest; which doesn't give you time to think too much about why you are rushing to put yourself within range of a lot of people who don't like you – really don't like you – and have guns in their hands.

Eventually we get the show on the road, set heading, cross the border quickly and head south. Janeke checks in on the radio, tells us the Can strike has gone in on target and the report from the recce team is that there is no noise from the camp area – sounds good, maybe they really are all dead. He asks for my time on target. The Dakota comes up to tell us he is loitering out to the west over the Limpopo River, and is our ToT still the same? I check my watch and give our estimate again. Red section – the Hunters – check in, all very clipped and professional, they'd be out to the west at high level to conserve fuel and so prolong their loiter time, can we confirm our ToT is still 0700?

Up where all the fixed wings are, it is daytime, they're basically in the cruise, the aircraft is trimmed out and it's all pretty relaxed. We're down on the treetops, it's still dark, you need both hands on the controls, and you're holding a map, trying to navigate over completely featureless terrain, and everybody keeps asking me my revised ToT.

"Standby." I check my watch again, do a quick calculation in my head, "that doesn't seem right", check my watch again. Whoops, now along with everything else I've got to wind the clock, it has stopped – talk about working like a one-armed paperhanger.

"Standby all aircraft for a time check. On my mark it is six fifty-two exactly. Three, two, one, mark. Time on target is oh seven hundred." That'll give them all something to do; they can all change their clocks. Life as a professional! Include in checks: wind your clock!!!

We get to the pan; the camp is on the south eastern corner, close to the railway line, and, of course, the rising sun is in the east also, straight in our eyes. However, it is better than crossing the heavily defended railway line, and with the dust in the air the sun is still low enough not to be causing a significant problem. I start climbing, aiming to be at about twelve hundred feet overhead initially. For fireforce work I generally like to be at five to six hundred feet; the recommended height is eight hundred and fifty and this is what the gunsight is calibrated for, but I prefer to be lower and see the bad guys. For this exercise, though, I want to be out of the way to start with, and once we confirm there are no cross bunnies on the ground we'll go a bit lower to direct the helicopters and control the sweep line through the camp.

Bert establishes comms with Schulie – I can hear the exchange through my headset and their radio is really on its last legs. We get their position marked on our air photo in case we lose comms altogether, and tell them they'll be picked up towards the end of the exercise and if they lose comms to throw a smoke if a helicopter looking to land comes in close to where they are. We come over the top of the camp, and can't see any movement. Janeke comes up and asks for a sitrep.

"It's all very quiet; I'm just going to give it a quick rev and see what happens."

Bert is still talking to Schulie and drowns out the reply, which is something about not wasting too much 20mm.

"John, give it a good hosing down, right through the middle." JB lifts himself in the seat and gets about three bursts out before the world erupts.

"Jesus fucking Christ." There is a massive explosion in the cockpit; bits of glass, metal and plastic are all over the place. Bert looks at me with eyes as wide as the proverbial dinner plates.

"I think I've been hit!" a screech from Bert, who then shuts up.

Great streaks of white flak are circling the helicopter, and I hear several small arms hits down the fuselage. JB's next bursts fly skywards as I break hard right, drop the collective and start down fast, getting as close to a half roll and pull through that an Alouette is ever going to. The streaks stay with us, and now we were pointing straight at a four-barrelled anti-aircraft gun dug in by the railway line. I clearly see the muzzle flashes as it opens up with great thumping sounds as the rounds whistle by.

"Pink lead hold off! Hold off! Go into an orbit and stay away from the pan."

"K2 get down on the deck! Stay down!"

Jesus. About ten seconds have gone by since we opened fire. Simmo's calm voice comes over the air, "I'm already down here, boy, when are you coming down?"

We are about halfway down, turning and descending as fast as we can to change the target picture for the flak, but have to continue down to about two hundred feet before we break lock with it.

I ease out towards the southwest, brushing through the treetops. I look at my newly wound watch; less than a minute has gone by, I can't believe we are still alive and airborne. We start to take stock.

I call the Hunters, who start rapidly descending towards a perch; then Pink leader, and tell him to push off home.

Janeke breaks in and asks what is going on; why is a Hunter strike needed and wouldn't it be better if the G-Cars go into an orbit and wait whilst the Hunters sort things out, then they can reapproach and drop the troops? In one of those ludicrous things that happen in moments of terror, I have an instant image of the old Japanese joke where the suicide pilot is told by his admiral to attack a US battleship – "Are you flucking mad?" – but then realise that other than Simmo and the recce team on the ground, nobody else knows what has just occurred.

"Sir, we've just had the biggest snottie from this place, we were very nearly taken out of the sky – there's no way we are going to get these troops on the ground. They've got some bloody big guns going in there – I think 23s and maybe bigger – and I got pulled badly by some dug-in stuff along the railway line. We've been hit quite badly, and we're going to have trouble getting the recce team off the ground. I need the Hunters in now and Pink should push off before their fuel becomes a problem, they can't help here."

"OK, but you'll need the G-Cars to extract the ground team."

"Negative – those guns cover right across the pan, they'll just take the G-Cars out. Get the Hunters to suppress the flak and we'll pull them out in the gunships."

Schulie is croaking through the radio to make sure we don't forget to pick him up, he is getting intermittent comms and has heard the G-Cars being ordered off but missed the next bit; he and Stephen are understandably not keen on getting left behind. Bert is briefing him to standby and on what is going to happen. I call Simmo and check his fuel state, and we make a plan to run in and pick the team up once the Hunters have sorted out the guns. Red lead calls and asks if the target could be marked with smoke. I tell him no fucking way are we going to try and put a smoke generator near the place, but to call me when he's ready to turn in live and we'll pop up, put some twenty mill in as a marker and I'll try to redirect the number two from his strike.

Red calls in live. We run in fast off the camp, pull up and slap some twenty mill in from absolute max range, getting a very angry response in return. Red sees either our strikes or the muzzle flashes and gets into the game. Basically they're on target, so the corrections for the number two and subsequent attacks are just to hose the whole camp over.

Janeke has got a back-up pair of Hunters airborne and a third pair is being brought up to readiness. Red finish off their ammunition in about four runs and shortly after their departing, Blue section arrives and starts working the camp over. Amazingly, as we are watching the attacks, the anti-aircraft is being directed towards the aircraft in the dive, and as he pulls up and away, the firing ceases and all the guns redirect towards the number two together. It is very disciplined, very frightening to watch, and the volume doesn't seem to be diminishing too much. Janeke comes up again and asks if the reserve Canberra would be any use, as it still has a full bomb load.

"Great, if it can get back here soon and just drop over the camp. We've got to stabilise this so we can go in for the pick-up, we're starting to get tight on fuel." He goes off frequency to organise this. Blue push off and there is a delay of a few minutes whilst the third pair of Hunters get to us; they've done bloody well to get along so fast. Simmo and I go over the plan to pull the guys off the ground. Bert briefs them on what is going to happen, and we start worrying big time, as it is looking as though we'll have to go in without the guns being neutralised, and they have an absolute clear field of fire across the pan.

White section arrives and starts. They have come armed only with front gun; they obviously didn't delay to fit SNEB pods, which is a good decision. We are getting very tight on fuel and decide to run in for our pick-up during their attack and hope the guns are too pre-occupied to notice us on the other side of the pan. The number two is Chris Abrams, an ex Royal Air Force Vulcan pilot of all backgrounds. On his dive, I think he's been hit; the aircraft goes very low short of the camp and I see the tail tuck badly, it must be very close to a high-speed stall. He gives his whole load of 30 mill in one continuous burst. For attacking point targets, you need to be diving at a high angle to minimise the spread of the rounds, but for strafing, a low angle is more effective as the rounds go through the target area until they hit something. The camp lights up with exploding 30 mill, and the A/A firing finally stops. The Hunter has four 30mm ADEN cannon packaged in a pod in the nose. Much is made of modern gatling type guns with rotating cannons, giving them a high rate of fire. Each ADEN has a rate of fire of 1,200 rounds per minute, and has a load of 120 rounds, so one six second burst with all four going gets a lot of attention on the ground.

We call Schulie and run in for the hot-extraction. At the pick-up point Schulie goes to Simmo's aircraft and leaps aboard. Stephen comes to us, and stands for a moment looking at the crowded cockpit in complete bewilderment; there is no room for him. A 12.7 starts up from the camp, way off initially, but the rounds are starting to creep towards us.

"JB, get him in!" I shout, and big John Britton leans out over the gun, grabs Stephen's shirt and hauls him, pack and rifle, draping him over the barrel of the gun as we lift off and stagger airborne, turning as quickly as possible away from the camp and railway line towards home. We are accelerating really slowly, and drawing small arms fire all the time from the bush – reinforcements must have been on their way down to the pan from the north. JB finally manhandles Stephen aboard.

We are both really short of fuel now, and everywhere we turn seems to attract a snottie of automatic small arms. I call for a fuel check and Simmo, like us, is well into red light.

The Dak calls and reminds us that he has fuel on board and if we can land in the Limpopo River he'll drop it right to us. I briefly consider this but fancy getting as close to the border as possible, and ask Janeke to get the G-Cars airborne with troops on board to give us some protection when we land, which we were going to have to do in the next couple of minutes. There is some chattering going on on the radio, so we can't speak for a minute or so, during which time we cross a cut line.

"What was that?" from Simmo

"The border, I think."

As I am about to suggest we land at the next clearing of

any size, a group of tents appears dead on the nose; trucks, Rhodesian soldiers.

Deep breath, super cool, calm and collected, "OK twelve o' clock on the nose, there's fuel here." We've hit the border patrol's camp.

After shutting down, Simmo comes over, "How the fuck did you navigate through that?"

"Benefit of a naval training."

More truthfully, why use skill when you can rely on luck? I hadn't navigated anywhere; I wasn't even totally sure we'd crossed the border.

Bert, in fact, hasn't been wounded. A 12.7 round has come through the floor and smacked his armoured seat right in the middle, which threw him upwards against the straps. I think he'd hit his head on one of the radios in the roof smashing it, and of course he had a very sore backside. But at least he still only has one hole in it.

It is about nine o' clock in the morning and we are totally shagged. We all wander around whilst the army rustle up some tea and sarnies, checking the surprisingly little damage on the aircraft and surreptitiously making sure there have been no accidents in our underpants, stopping hyperventilating and, generally, feeling very, very lucky. We are just about to find out how wrong we are.

I call Janeke and gave him a sitrep on where we are.

"Mike, did you ever make comms with the Can?"

To be honest, I've forgotten all about it and say that I haven't heard him on the radio and he certainly didn't pass through whilst we were in the vicinity of the camp.

"Well, he turned back and was descending for his IP, since

when nobody's heard from him. I've checked with Salisbury, Thornhill and Chiredzi, and there's been no call. When you've refuelled, the rest of the choppers are at Malapati, get there ASAP."

I tell the rest that the Can has gone missing, and most of the survival euphoria disappears. We refuel and trundle over to Malapati. Schulie and Stephen say thanks and depart with Bert, and the rest of us settle in to wait. The aircraft are fuelled and rearmed and we hang around the ops tent, listening to various radio reports coming in reference the missing Can. The Scouts' assault team stays with us, in case we need to get a protection team in somewhere.

Fixed wing aircraft are up listening for transmissions on 121.5, the distress frequency of the pilots' survival beacons, but nothing is heard. Eventually the time for the Can to have run out of fuel passes, and a full check of even remote airfields had been carried out in the hope that the crew have made a forced landing somewhere. Then comes a report from Vila Salazar, the Rhodesian town opposite Malvernia, that a policeman saw an aircraft flying low over Malvernia, drawing a lot of fire and turning hard, and he had seen pieces flying off. Often, when reported by non-aviation people, this can be the canopy and ejection seats going. Anyway, it now seems certain that for some reason the Can had been over Malvernia and has been shot down.

Janeke lands, gets together with Simmo and me and suggests that we take the formation of helicopters in a low-level line abreast sweep to the west of Malvernia to see if we can locate any wreckage or the crew. You are normally more likely to see wreckage from a higher level, but the Hunters have already been over the area, and unfortunately there was so much cloud cover at about fifteen hundred to two thousand feet that they couldn't see too much of the ground.

Nobody is chomping at the bit to fly low-level in the vicinity of Malvernia, but we cobble together a plan where we'll do a battle echelon starboard – echelon being a much easier formation to maintain than line abreast. Pete and I will be on the flanks with the gunships, and the G-Cars will be carrying the assault troops in case we need to land, with orders that they are cleared to fire from the aircraft at will, which is normally not allowed. Having swept across once, we'll do a long right hand turn, reorganise into echelon port and come back towards the border, this time with Pete leading on the flank nearest Malvernia.

Somebody has located some burning bush through binoculars from one of the fixed wings, and we are particularly interested in this area.

The sweeps are carried out, in fact without attracting an awful lot of ground fire either way as it happens, and we have a good look at the burning bush area. However, we see nothing resembling pieces of aircraft, and nobody gets a squeak on 121.5. As far as I know, the wreck has never been located.

In the following days, there is much speculation about what had occurred, and the odd uncalled-for comment about Air-Sub Lieutenant Dave Hawkes being a very inexperienced navigator. My own view, and I think probably it was the official one in the end, is that in a hurry to get back to the action they descended fast on a rough heading to get to the general vicinity of their IP, intending to get a positive fix below cloud. That's what I and just about anybody else would have done, and been expected to do, no matter what one's experience. Unfortunately, they broke cloud right overhead Malvernia, and collected the full works. It would be a natural reaction to break hard when confronted by a wall of flak, and it is possible that the Can actually broke-up by being overstressed rather than being shot down; the air force had previously lost Canberras due to overstressing. Also, with Malvernia being a relatively small place, you are actually keeping yourself in the dwang by turning and it might have been better to just fly straight across once the error had been made.

Unfortunately, whatever happened, Ian Donaldson had only about the time it has taken to read this sentence to decide what to do.

Subsequent intelligence showed that in between the plan's conception and its execution, or attempted execution, the camp had been reinforced with a newly trained specialist anti-aircraft unit with East German instructors. Their fire had certainly been disciplined and well-directed, which was something we had not come up against before. As it turned out, the alphas had, in fact, caused a lot of mayhem, but it was only after a couple of other bombing attacks were analysed that it was realised why we weren't getting quite the results that had been expected. The bombs were designed to explode and throw shrapnel at body height. By attacking at night when most of the enemy were lying down, the shrapnel was passing over the top of them. The modus operandi was modified so that attacks commenced with an element of 1 Squadron initiating proceedings at first shooting light by taking out anti-aircraft weapons identified off air photographs, with the secondary objective of giving everybody a wake-up call and getting them up and running around. The Cans would then run over the top with their load before they had time to get into bunkers and trenches. This method also gave the Canberra crews a visual target marker on which to adjust the final bomb run. The K-Cars would arrive next, with the camp hopefully softened up. It relied on well co-ordinated timings of the respective formations, and mostly worked really well on these early attacks. Having devised a good tactic, however, the Rhodesian planners never modified it, and the tactic used right up to the end of the war of attacking heavily defended external camps with a jet strike and then sending in soft-skinned, slow-moving helicopters to do the 'mopping-up' became practically criminal in its idiocy.

CHAPTER TEN

Mavue

After four days of intensive flying in support of Operation Mardon, north of the border in Mocambique, we recover to Mount Darwin after last light, just outrunning a pretty tasty looking thunderstorm approaching from the other direction. All thoughts of a day of rest are immediately allayed with two fireforce callouts in quick succession the following day.

I am then tasked with flying to Mtoko, so load up with Doris and flog over to FAF 5.

Arriving at last light, I am immediately retasked to drop Hans Steyn, the gunner, and continue without a crewman to Fort Victoria. Who on earth thinks up these arrangements? I've flown fifteen hours in the last two days, and am certainly not going to night fly down to Fort Vic now. I draft a signal to hindquarters with a flight plan from Mtoko to Salisbury, overnight at Salisbury and early morning departure for Fort Victoria, and tell the ops room to wait until I am airborne before sorting out 'the difficulty in getting the teleprinter to operate'. As it happens, nobody actually gives a damn, the whole thing was probably thought up by an RWS corporal; there is a signal waiting for me at Sarum. I have to pick up three technician/ gunners at Fort Victoria and be at Chiredzi at lunch time tomorrow. Basically, I am running a taxi service around the country, positioning Hansie at Mtoko, and Flamo, Tony Jordan and another tech at Chiredzi. The staff who institute these arrangements never seem to appreciate that we are shagged out, particularly after a high-density operation like Mardon. There may be some saving in fuel or something chugging us around the bush instead of arranging some courier pilots from the Police Air Wing to position aircrew, but the effect on morale and the overall tiredness of the pilots on bush tours far outweighs this.

Despite all my whinging about tiredness, I manage to make the most of an overnight stop in Bright Lights, yawning my way through a couple of favourite bars and finding an accommodating stress counsellor, whose husband is away, after only a couple of phone calls.

Arriving at Chiredzi, the orders change again and I am told to crew a K-Car that is sitting there idle. I carry my full mappage for the whole country with me after a bush trip some time back. Mike Upton and I were sent to Kanyemba to cover a Scouts, external recce for three days max! It is over six weeks before I get back to Sarum, after an odyssey across the north of the country, down through Matabeleland and then eastwards back to Chiredzi. I start off with a one to one million map of Rhodesia, which is about as useful for helicopter operations as a page from 'Your First Atlas'. I do acquire some odd maps along the way, including a delightful antique down in the south-west that has the enchantingly vague term 'high ground here' marked on it, with no indication whether we are talking of Alpine towers or rolling hills. It turns out to be a barely perceptible rise in the ground in the flatlands of cattle country. Ever since then, I've carried a full set of maps with me, and one in fifty thou coverage of the adjoining three or four areas that I should be operating in.

The trip starts off pleasantly enough – we are to go to Kariba and liaise with the chopper there. We set off low-level across the Zambezi basin. The valley floor is full of game – tourists would pay a fortune for a flight like this. This particular flight teaches me to always carry a camera in the future. We are pretty blasé about game viewing, but cracking out over the mopani into a wide vlei we come across a lioness and two cubs. Neither of us has a camera. The lioness shepherds the two cubs into a thorn bush and sits watching us as we circle her. As we hover closer she sits in that inscrutable feline way: "I'm not in the slightest bit interested in your games, and am not leaving these cubs, but you come just a teensy bit nearer and you are going to save me looking for lunch!" I realise that a leap of ten feet up into the open door is conceivably not beyond her, and decide that it's time to push off. A bit later we come across a troop of baboons, and manage to cut the leader away from the others and spend a few minutes chasing him around. We are much closer to him than the lioness, and I definitely see him gauging the distance to the aircraft step. The thought of a pissed-off monkey with three inch fangs bouncing around the aircraft is no more appealing than the lioness, so we stop terrorising him and continue on a magnificent game-viewing ride. This is the area of one of Africa's best game parks – Mana Pools – which, due to the war, has hardly been visited for years, and is abundant in the whole variety of animals indigenous to this part of the continent.

When we arrive at Kariba, there are two other helicopters already there, piloted by Gaps Newman and Greg Todd. There is a complicated crew and aircraft change, and as one of the aircraft goes tech, we end up with all three crews staying the night. FAF 2 is not functioning, so the duty helicopter is parked at night on the basketball court at the army base on the heights in Kariba Town. The army start flapping about where we are going to park the other aircraft and are suitably impressed when, with a bit of respotting of two shut-down aircraft on the court, we make room for the third to squeeze in.

Gaps and Grog, my new gunner Dave Jenkie and Mike Upton are none of them known for advocating tee-totalism, and we have a suitably lubricated night around the hotels and casinos of Kariba.

Dude Thomas has ejected from a Hunter a day or so previously, and when we return to the army camp the signaller hands us an instruction from the air force. Having divested himself of his parachute, Dude had discovered that his mini-flare cartridges, for marking his position for the rescue helicopter, were not compatible with the flare gun, so we are all instructed to check our survival kits for flare/launcher compatibility.

No time like the present. We all duly fumble our flare kits out of our survival kits in the aircraft and screw on a cartridge. They are all fine. But now they are ready to fire we may as well check the whole mechanism works, and launch six flares out across the lake. This looks really nice, and we hear some 'ahhs' from some locals at the nearby hotel. In the interests of public morale, we reload and send off another salvo. And then a few more, until surprise, surprise, we are out of flares.

Or at least mini-flares. We also have a verey pistol in each aircraft that fires bigger flares. And a few 'Icarus' parachute flares. And some smoke grenades. And some 'Instant Light' grenades. So we are able to put on quite a firework display. Having verified that all our flares and grenades work, we check out our pistol ammunition – all serviceable, and then our rifle ammunition, a certain amount of which is tracer, so we are back to the pyrotechnic display. Mike Upton is fumbling with the MAG on one of the helicopters before we decide that perhaps it is time to call a halt and go to bed.

The basketball court resembles the Alamo on the morning after, covered with doppies and burnt out grenades, and we have to negotiate seriously with the army about resupplying all our pyrotechnics; the ammunition isn't such a problem. We eventually swap a complete resupply against lifting a biltong team into the valley to shoot a buffalo, transport the meat back to the camp and dispose of the horns, hooves and other 'evidence' that National Parks would be interested in, far out over the water.

The others depart and Jenkie and I settle into a few days at Kariba. I'm a bit concerned that we have been given no indication of our changeover date, but Jenkie explains that it can only be in a few days as he is about to go on overseas leave with Brenda, his new wife. Anyway, who can complain about a few days at Kariba?

The resident company commander asks us to do some enplaning and deplaning drills for his troops, so we give the lectures, show them in groups around the helicopter to point out the danger zones when running in and out of the helicopter and organise a routine whereby we will enplane each stick normally at the barracks, hover jump them out at the airfield, then pick up the previous stick and redeliver them to the barracks on the heights. This is a valuable exercise. The RLI, Scouts, RAR and SAS are all very comfortable and proficient around the aircraft, as they are operating with them regularly, but we often find ourselves called to ambushes or contacts with the independent companies or PATU sticks, that are largely made up of youngsters doing their national service or people on call-up duties who are not familiar with leaping in and out of helicopters. The general noise and lack of visibility due to dust and brush being thrown around by the rotor downwash adds to the confusion and apprehension of being in close proximity to the enemy, and people very easily forget that the main blades can flap up and down drastically in certain circumstances, bringing your head fatally close to them, particularly if the ground is sloping or uneven. A surprising number of men exit the aircraft and run towards the tail, despite being warned of the lethal presence of the tail rotor, and people forget that even a rifle held vertically can easily contact the main rotor blades. Aside from the certain terminal effects of these actions for the perpetrator, it is most probable that it will cause the helicopter to spin out of control on the ground, beat itself to death and send items of high speed rotating machinery in all directions.

There is always somebody in these sessions that has done it all before, and sure enough we have one here who is waiting in ambush with all the smart questions. He's not out to impress us so much as to be the big deal among his mates.

We start the flying exercise and move the first three sticks down to the airfield – about a five-minute hop from the barracks, with no problems. On fireforce duties, the RLI, of course, are often out of the chopper and away into the bush before we have finished flaring to land, but the SOP is for the troops to wait until they get a positive thumbs up from the tech or pilot, or if the aircraft is in a low hover, the pilot will signal the OK by nodding his head.

As we run in for the fourth time, the daily Air Rhodesia Viscount has just disembarked its passengers. We are at about twenty feet descending and decelerating to come to the hover at about six to eight feet for the troops to jump out.

"Isn't that Janet Shirley?" Jenkie says, referring to the blonde air hostess standing at the aircraft steps.

I look over, "Yeah, maybe we'll land and go over for some tea," I reply, but unfortunately nod my head in conjunction with the "yeah".

The stick leader, poised behind me, launches himself out of the blocks like a released greyhound, and arrives in a crumpled heap on the deck. It is, naturally, Mr Smarty Pants, and he has broken both ankles, so the arriving passengers are witness to a live casevac up to the hospital on the heights, and we miss out on our tea and biccies.

Sadly, two days later we are back at the hospital again, initially to casevac a patient down to a fixed wing aircraft at the airfield. The patient is a highly decorated, legendary founder member of the Selous Scouts, 'Stretch' Franklin, and he has been seriously injured in a motorcycle accident – the bike having skidded off the switchback road down from the heights, and tumbled a way down the mountain. It has been decided to casevac him to Andrew Fleming hospital in Salisbury.

On arrival at Kariba airfield, they cannot get the stretcher into the puss-cat PRAW aircraft that is going to take him and the nursing sister. Jenkie looks at taking the door off and some seats out, but even then the stretcher is not going to fit, the man is about six foot six. Jenkie tops us off with fuel and we rig the stretcher in the back of the chopper – the sister suspending his drips from the aircraft roof – and set off for Salisbury. I get Jenks to secure the blankets over the stretcher; the last thing we need is one of them blowing back into the tail rotor. We hit some mean weather on the way down and then about three quarters of an hour out of Salisbury the sister starts to get very agitated – the patient has taken a turn for the worse and is going down fast. His heart has stopped, and she and Jenkie are doing CPR. I radio ahead to Salisbury tower and tell them to inform Andrew Fleming to have an emergency team waiting for us on the pad.

Jenkie tells me that he's dead. He knows him well and tears are streaming down his face. I turn around and the sister is crying too. I scream at her to get back on the CPR and keep it up until we get to the hospital, it's not her job to decide who is dead and when. The weather is appalling, and because of the headwind we are now running short of fuel. When the red 'fuel low' warning light comes on, we have ten minutes of safe flying left. We drag in over the northern suburbs with me waiting for the engine to fail and prepared for an instant auto rotation, and get onto the pad after fifteen minutes, red light. The hospital crash team are there and work frantically for about half an hour. Eventually the doctor calls it a day; he really is dead.

I call Sarum and explain that I need fuel at the hospital. It takes a couple of hours for a vehicle to arrive, and then it has only got one drum aboard, so by the time we have flogged over to Sarum and topped up we are faced with night flying back to Kariba. Normally, we'd jump at the chance of a Salisbury night stop, but there is a party in Kariba that night, so having checked the bad weather has passed along, we make the obvious decision and set sail to the north-west. After all, you can hardly get lost; there's a set of massive power lines that lead to Kariba dam, so if you find yourself crossing them, just turn to fly along them, and at the end, there is either a massive lake or a big river.

There was an occasion with a South African pilot who, instead of lining his maps up and drawing in a course of roughly north-west, laid them on top of each other, drew in a northerly course and then confidently 'map read' his way to the edge of the escarpment – and then further, assuming that the lake level was low, which was why the shore was not in sight, and eventually put down at a remote police post when he ran out of fuel. The chap could barely speak English, and it took several hours to sort out and get fuel to him, but he was a rather special person and prone to many self-induced misadventures.

Our plan doesn't look so clever a couple of hours later. The weather is generally OK, but the visibility is shocking due to smoke from bush fires and low-level dust haze. We do actually miss seeing the power lines, and then start to cross a big river. Jenkie is convinced that the Zambezi is the only big river in the region and that I am hijacking him to Zambia. I am sure it is not the Zambezi because of the angle we crossed it, although on my 'Child's Atlas' chart I can't find an alternative. I make a deal with him that if we don't get a positive fix in the next ten minutes I'll turn around and we'll land on the right bank of the river and wait for daylight. The seeds of doubt have been sown, and I spend the next ten minutes concocting geometric patterns in my head and seriously wondering if we haven't been blown down to the western end of the lake by a rogue crosswind, and it was the Zambezi after all. The nurse, of course, is oblivious to all of this and smiles cheerfully each time we look at her, she's more worried about keeping us from looking up her skirt as the slipstream blows it around. About the same time as Jenkie is about to get his pistol out and insist on turning around we pick up the lights of Bumi and call in at the police LZ for a top-up of fuel. We have in fact been blown a little to the west, and the 'big' river, which in fact doesn't compare with the Zambezi at all, was the Sanyati.

The police are quite excited at our visit – they don't get a chopper in too often and are very keen to assist in the refuelling. They question us closely on the gooks' attack on Kariba a few nights back, and we are mystified for a while until we realise they had seen our fireworks display. They are keen for us to stay the night – I think it is rather more to do with the nursing sister than our presence – but now we're fat on fuel and know where we are it's a short hop around the lake to the party at the casino, and following the lake shore even I can't go astray.

The following day we are away on a minor casevac, and return to find Flight Sergeant Butch Graydon, Jenkie's replacement, waiting for us. The courier flight that he came up on was being flown by an SAP pilot and he refused to wait for Jenkie to return. I'm also given a sealed envelope with coded orders. There are various coding systems we are supposedly conversant with. The only one we ever really use on fireforce is the 'shackle' code, which is a very simple substitution code and is changed daily. It changes at midnight every day and has normally been thoroughly compromised by any eavesdropping signals' intelligence gatherers by first light the same day. My own view is that the use of codes causes us more problems than it's worth, as our opposition is not in a position to react to any sigint it receives on a tactical basis. Coding is one of those things that the military insist on doing no matter whether it is efficient or not. If you speak in plain language, everybody knows what is going on; we had an incident a month or two back when Slade Healey was told to go to 'the place beginning with M – A – L' for a casevac. The ops room meant Mabalauta, which raises questions about their spelling abilities, but Slade flogged off to Malvernia, which proved that he could spell in English as well as Afrikaans, but should have raised doubts in other areas as Malvernia is in Mocambique and about the most heavily defended town on the border. Slade is actually making an approach to the airfield when an accompanying Lynx screams at him to break away. Frelimo hardly shoot at them, they were probably so astounded that it was happening that they thought it was a 'cunning trap'. Why not just tell him to go to Mabalauta?

Anyway, this signal is a real lulu. Some genius has invested a fortune of the air force's budget in a coding machine called Jupiter, which is now part of the helicopter's kit. We've all completed a course in operating this machine, which is about ten times more complicated than flying. We give up using them after a month. I finally get some sort of sense out of the message, which redirects me to another of our codes, the 'placard' system. This is like a treasure hunt. We finally hit on a destination of 'Grant's Junction', which is a railway siding on the line between Bulawayo and Victoria Falls on the other side of the country. Jenkie is seriously worried about his departure for Europe. There are no flights out of Kariba that will get him to Salisbury in time, and there's not a lot of traffic for hitching a lift. He decides to come with us as Grant's Junction is not that far out of Bulawayo and I promise him I'll get him there by the following morning at the latest. The three of us trog off on an epic cross-country flight, refuelling at odd police stations and eventually following the railway line towards Bulawayo.

We arrive at Grant's Junction, to find that the task which we are there for has been cancelled a couple of days previously – it was to assist the local police in a murder enquiry. It is coming up to sunset, we've been flying all day and a night at Grant's Junction is not too appealing. Jenkie is really concerned about his whereabouts now, and rather more about how he is going to explain to Brenda that he is actually getting further and further away from her.

Butch and I have been pulling his leg all day about him missing his trip, it has been the main means of staving off boredom in the long haul around the country, but I take pity and we night fly into Bulawayo – secure the aircraft at the airport and book into the Holiday Inn, arranging for the bill to be sent to the commander of the air force. We organise a flight up to Salisbury on Air Rhodesia for Dave – chitty to the commander – the following day, and Butch and I proceed as per new orders to Gwanda.

Matabeleland has not seen a helicopter for some while and somebody makes a decision for us to stay down here. There are no fuel dumps in this part of the world, so the helicopter gets quite used to running on diesel, picked up from mines, logging camps and the like, signed for by me on behalf of the commander. Many people are disbelieving when we fill up with diesel – including more than once at roadside filling stations – but it is very similar to jet fuel, and the engine works quite happily on it – the filters have to be changed more regularly is the main problem.

We spend six weeks trundling around the south-west of the country. I meet and fall in love with a rancher's daughter – she is still at school, which makes me some sort of dirty old man – but it is real. None of the, mainly, police units and odd army outposts have had the use of a helicopter for years, but once they have, we apparently become indispensable, and somebody has the clout to keep us there. I do get rather concerned when I phone through to the squadron to order a spare part, and Boss Harold asks me where we are and when we're coming back. He's asking me? I thought the tasking was coming from him.

So after this bush trip I always pack all my maps, a camera and a standard bush kit, no matter if it is planned for three days or a month.

★

When I arrive at Chiredzi, there is a detachment of three G-Cars being run by 'Grimshag', Squadron Leader Graham Cronshaw, who at this time is an ex 7 Squadron 'heavy' doing a turn in the bush from his headquarters job. As there is no fireforce operating here, the K-Car is unmanned, but an external raid is about to be mounted and it needs to be manned. I defer to his experience and suggest that he leads as the senior officer, but he declines the offer and I find I don't even get to choose the best gunner, as he doesn't want to split his 'team' up as they are working together so well.

The target is a camp over the border from the south-east corner of Rhodesia – Mavue. The air force is going to bomb with the Canberras, take out the triple-a with Hunter strikes and then drop in six Dak loads of SAS paratroops, backed up with some heliborne troops from our G-Cars, and controlled by Major Barney Robinson, 22's commanding officer, in the K-Car.

During the briefing it quickly becomes apparent that there are not enough helos, and after a bit of wrangling it is agreed that we will combine with the Chipinga fireforce. However, the jet jockeys and the planners are not keen on delaying the briefing, so I am told to brief them when we join up at Mutandawhe just prior to the strike. This does not seem like a good idea; why can't we do it properly and get everybody here and hearing the same story? I'm told to wind my neck in. The impression is very much that the helicopter part of the deal is a side-show to the jet strikes and the parachute assault.

The aerial photos show firstly that the camp is hard to pick out of the flat bush of the area and, secondly, that there are some tasty anti-aircraft defences dug in around the perimeter. The whole complex is a network of trenches and bunkers. We are paying very close attention, but the jet drivers are very gung-ho. The Cans are going in first with their new alpha bombs. They have evolved a tactic where they drop whilst flying in close echelon, which gives carpet coverage of an area as large as this camp complex. The Hunters will use this strike as the marker for their own attack thirty seconds later, using their own photos to locate their specific targets around the perimeter of the devastation caused by the bomb strike.

Thirty seconds on from this the Dakotas will be running in for their para drop; the two K-Cars – me and whoever is flying the Chipinga gunship – will pull up over the top of the para drop for Robinson to organise his paratroops and deploy the heliborne troops as required.

Easy-peasy. OK, quick cup of coffee then we're back to Sarum/Thornhill, we'll be exactly on ToT so don't you helicopters be late.

Questions? Oh, questions. Right.

I ask if any of the Hunters will be carrying frantan. The answer is no. They will all be carrying SNEB – 68mm rockets

– as they have to take out point defences, and they are able to deliver the rockets with more precision. 1 Squadron are great on precision. Some months previously, in response to an article in a South African magazine commenting on the air–ground gunnery skills of their pilots being so good they could 'shoot up a dustbin in a jungle clearing', Squadron Leader Rich Brand did just that, getting a DH with just five rounds on a dustbin at Kutanga Range.

I keep on, and with some backing from Barney Rubble, we don't like the look of those gun pits and trenches at all. The planners are convinced that after the alpha bombs and Hunter strikes, there will be nobody left fighting. I get a lecture from the Hunter boss about the relative merits of SNEB and frantan. I know this, I used to drop the bloody things, but we are not whistling by at 450 knots with an armoured windscreen and bang seat; I've been caught before in a soft-skinned helicopter by dug-in troops with heavy machine guns, and know that the one thing guaranteed to spoil their day is a lot of sticky fire thrown all over them.

Eventually, with the intervention of Tol Janeke, the ranking officer, a compromise is reached, and the two Lynxes will drop their rocket pods and carry four small frantan canisters each. The Lynxes – Black Section – are being flown by Mike Delport and Clive Ward, who is actually a 3 Squadron Dakota captain, but the bush squadrons are so short of pilots he is doing a stint on 4 Squadron and being shown the ropes by Mike.

We finish with the palaver of synchronising watches, good lucks all round, the jet contingent push off to prepare for tomorrow and we are left to get ourselves set up for the strike in the morning.

Wrong. Just as lunch time comes around there is a call for fireforce and we spend the rest of the afternoon chasing gooks around Mashoko Mission. The poor old techs really get the hind tit on these occasions, as not only do they have their flying duties, on recovery to the FAF they have to get the aircraft lubed, repaired and ready for launch the next day. It always amazes me how they unfailingly, and generally cheerfully, manage to do this.

★

We are off before first light in order to give us time to brief the Chipinga reinforcements and get ourselves organised at Mutandawhe so we don't foul up getting to the match on time.

Janeke comes with us in his personal Cessna and is almost apoplectic when the Chipinga formation arrives and they climb out looking like a band of Yugoslav partisans. Willie Knight is even wearing a sleeveless sheepskin waistcoat over his shirt, and they are all unshaven and bedraggled. He calms down quickly, though, when he learns that we are lucky they are here at all; they were out fighting until after dark and spent the night laagered up at a police station in the hills to make sure they got here on time, which also involved flying through some dodgy weather in the mountains.

We go through the game plan and sort out the team positions. I am going to lead, carrying Brian Robbie and my gunner Steve Russell; Chris Dickinson will fly the second K-Car with Captain Scotty McCormack as the deputy SAS commander, and Graham Cronshaw declines my last ditch offer of the gunship and will organise the G-Car Formation – Pink – of six. The Cans' callsign is Green, the Hunters, two sections of two, Red and Blue, and the Dakotas, Silver.

I get Steve Russell to top off the fuel with a couple of hundred extra pounds of 'insurance' and to put two extra cases of 20mm shells in the cockpit. Cronshaw tells him to take it out as we will be overweight, but Steve sneaks it back in again after he has wandered back to his own aircraft.

We launch and reach our IP, which is far enough from the border that the gooks will not hear us, and go into a holding orbit. As I am heading north-west, I see the Dakotas appear over the horizon in a six-ship vic formation – what a great sight – and on the same orbit, but now heading south, see a massive eruption in the direction of the camp – the Can strike – but not the aircraft. We start our run in and I hear Red calling in live. Then Green come up, and say they didn't see the target. There's a couple of snappy exchanges, Blue have put in their strike and we are starting to pull up, when Red says that he's got the camp visual – what does he mean he's got it visual, what did he have the first time? He's going to restrike. Silver lead in the Dakotas comes in and says they are starting their drop run. A lot of flak and tracer starts up from the camp. Red insists on restriking and tells Silver to hold off. Cronshaw has already had the sense to orbit the G-Cars and Toffo and I turn hard left under the Dakota formation as it waffles around in its ungainly entirety – these poor buggers haven't flown formation in yonks, and now they're doing an air show.

Red and Blue restrike a couple of times. They are trying hard to recorrect from each other's strikes, but the flak seems to be getting worse rather than better. We can see what has happened: the Canberra strike has gone in alongside the camp, the right-hand edge of the strike just touching the left-hand edge of the camp. The initial Hunter strikes had gone onto the right areas as applied to the Can strike but, of course, the guns weren't there. The jets' ammunition is expended and Red lead hands over to us. What the jet strike has managed to do, of course, is make sure everybody is awake and given time for them to get into the trenches. In all fairness, they have taken out a number of the guns but there are still a few left and Chris and I are taking a multitude of hits.

Robbie wants his paratroops on the ground, but it is going to take some minutes for that formation to complete its orbit and reposition for a new drop. We can see the gooks starting to break out of the camp and leg it into the surrounding bush. We decide to switch targets from the guns and get some rounds down to stop this exodus.

"Steve. Fire at those running gooks. Quickly, man."

Poor Steve Russell wears pretty substantial glasses.

"What shall I fire at?"

Christ, it looks like ants running out of an ant hill and he can't see them.

"Just pull the fucking trigger and wave the barrel around! Come on, man, open fire!"

Once he's got them visual he shoots well and the mad rush stops as they start to take cover.

We are getting some serious attention from a heavy weapon and we switch targets back to that. I look up and see Chris' cannon spitting at another gun on the opposite side of the orbit. Suddenly there is a horrific thumping very, very close to the helicopter; what on earth are they firing with and where is it coming from? I have a perfect side view of a Hunter, its wingtip about thirty feet in front of us pulling out of a strafing dive. The thumping was its 30 mill going past. He's nearly shot us down and then missed a collision by feet. I watch as he narrowly misses Chris as well on the pull-out.

I call Red Lead and tell him to keep his aircraft out of it. He tells me that they are just about to join the circuit at Thornhill.

"I don't fucking care if its Red or Blue, I've just nearly been shot down and then had a mid-air; clear off out of it and let us sort this mess out!"

Blue Lead calls up and says that his section is well away from the target and it is nothing to do with them.

"Just sod off!" We're getting into real trouble with very

heavy automatic small arms fire coming up from troops well protected in their trenches. The Daks fly through a curtain of green tracer and the troops tumble out.

I call for Black section and there is no reply. Delport coughs afterwards that he hoped he'd misheard, because he knew what was coming next. He answers the second time and I ask him to do a line-abreast low run over the camp and throw all the frans in one go. Poor old Clive, Black Two, was flogging his Dak around a week ago. They call in live and we stop firing as they run in from the east. Mike reckons it was the lowest he'd ever flown on an attack, but during the run-in he saw Clive alongside and slightly behind him even lower.

They deliver the weapons perfectly, Clive collects a 12.7 round through a tail boom and they both subsequently collect seriously deserved MFCs. The fire spreads over the trenches and the flak decreases to normal levels.

The gooks see they are being enveloped and start to gap it out to the bush again. I tell Steve to fire at will and start with Robbie to organise the paratroop sweeps and direct the G-Cars to drop their cut-off sticks. Robbie is purple with rage as he cannot contact his ground force commander, Captain John Murphy, a former US Marine Vietnam veteran. It transpires that he was hung up in a tree from the paradrop and spent most of the battle swinging on his harness and shooting with his pistol at gooks running underneath him.

I am looking out the other way when I hear Robbie's voice becoming really strangled – he sounds as though he's having a heart attack. As I look round, Steve is blasting away with the cannon and Robbie's mictel lead has caught in the feed belt. He's being dragged into the gun – the gun jams before he's squeezed into the breech and shot out – he's small enough, it might really happen!

We eventually get some order into this three-ring circus

and settle into a long day providing top cover for the ground sweeps, who have the unenviable task of moving into the camp and securing it. Each time they come up against some dug-in resistance or there is some nasty looking cover up ahead we use the K-Cars as mobile artillery and lay down fire for them. We are specifically forbidden to use 20 mill ammunition unless we have a definite target visual, but using the G-Cars' machine guns is useless for flushing fire. It doesn't matter how many times we state this, the orders remain the same on the basis that it is too expensive to use the 20 mill. We ignore it anyway; nobody out here is going to risk the troops' lives for some half-baked accountancy problem in hindquarters.

The camp is secured with no casualties on our side, a multitude on the other, most caused not as expected by the initial air strikes, but the ground troops in a myriad of vicious little firefights throughout the day. The helicopters are kept busy flying out documents and other intelligence material, a few prisoners and any salvageable weaponry and ammunition; Cronshaw organises all the G-Car work and does an excellent job, leaving Chris and I to sort out the close support work. By the time we get back to Chiredzi we have flown seven and a half hours, an hour of it at night. The temperature has been in the high thirties and low forties all day and we've had bugger-all to eat.

The FAF have hot meals waiting for us, however, and a monumental party takes place in the mess. Present is John Annan, the pilot of the mystery Hunter, who had launched as White section, an airborne reserve, had a radio transmission problem, heard the difficulties and decided to deliver his weaponry onto the target anyway. He admits he hadn't seen any other aircraft in the orbit, which is why he had attacked, and was astonished when he heard my screeching as he was pulling out, also not seeing Toffo in the other K-Car. The matter is finalised with a round of drinks.

We were back early the next day to cover the final
withdrawal of our troops and there was a perfunctory debrief
held at Chiredzi, unattended by the jet squadrons. Unbelievably
,there was an atmosphere of euphoria – the results had, in fact,
been pretty good – and nobody wanted to listen to the absolute
pig's ear of the first minutes after H-hour. Not for the first time
did it strike me that as far as the air force was concerned, there
were two separate wars going on. Putting a first pass jet strike
in featureless bush conditions is an incredibly difficult task, but
it is no good saying they only missed by yards. You can do that
shooting at dustbins on the range and it doesn't matter, do it for
real and the whole exercise is worse than pointless. Added to
that, once the sequence of events has been finalised, it is no good
the jets screwing the other formations around by insisting on
restriking; it's not a range practice and we would be better getting
the troops on the ground and using our own firepower, working
from the helicopters, before the enemy gets time to settle in. The
jet strike is a devastating way to initiate an attack but we have to
get a method of ensuring it is delivered on the nail.

The debrief comes to an end with a fireforce callout and we
spend the next five hours jousting in the Boli area. Back at FAF
7 in the evening I get the two airstrike reports written, before
slurping two beers and collapsing into bed, having flown
seventeen hours in two days.

★

Interestingly, Randy Du Rand, the Canberra boss, arrives with
a bombed-up aircraft two days later. He has read the comments
in the airstrike report and wants to see if we can devise a system
for marking a target for the Can for use in internal operations.

Our chance comes the following day. A Scouts' OP has a
ground team in close to a group of eight in a valley near Lake

MacDougall. We launch the fireforce and as we lift off, I notice the Can crew strolling over for another coffee; they don't have to think of taking off for another forty-five minutes. Initial exchanges with the OP establish that the ground team are a couple of hundred metres short of the gooks and I tell them that we will fly across the valley and drop a smoke generator onto the position they have given us for the gooks. They are to give me a correction for the target from the smoke and then to take really good cover as there is to be a 'Cyclone 5' dropping bombs. They are a bit mystified by this – they are used to Cyclones 7, us, 4, the Lynxes, 3, Dakotas, and the OP commander knows what a Cyclone 1 is, the Hunter, but I haven't time to explain as we are lining up for the smoke generator drop and the Can is now less than two minutes out.

We put the generator onto the given position and turn along the ridge to observe the target area – no smoke appears and I see the Can about five miles – one minute – away on his run. He calls doors open, and that he is not visual with smoke. I tell him to keep coming and about fifteen seconds before he has to abort, the ground callsign tell me the smoke is about fifty yards short of the target towards them. I still can't see any smoke, and then there is a thin stream coming through the trees.

"Target is plus fifty from the smoke. Plus fifty."

"Not visu…… ahh got it! Bombs gone."

My heart jumps; a dark cloud appears below the fast-moving jet and at first looks as though it will fall on our own ground callsign. But, of course, it is moving forwards at over three hundred knots and within seconds, a great swathe of bush erupts in flame and smoke.

"K-Car, Alpha Five. How was that?" from Randy.

"Alpha 5 standby. Two Four Zulu, Two Four Zulu, K-Car, are you OK?"

No answer. I repeat the call three times before they reply – they have been deafened by the blast and haven't heard us.

"K-Car, tha– tha– that was fan– fan– fantastic. But it was very, very close? What is that Ndege?"

We heave sighs of relief and order the group to sweep forward.

"Alpha 5, it was right on the coke, see you back at base."

Unfortunately, when we get back to Chiredzi it is to report that no bodies or casualties were found, but we agree the basis for co-ordinating the Can with the fireforce is there, and they depart back to Sarum as there are no more bombs available.

The good news comes in the morning. Overnight at a police post a group of eight has walked in and surrendered. They started moving up the side of the valley when they saw the smoke generator land, realising that something bad was about to happen. The jet strike missed them by yards, they are completely shell-shocked and want no further part in the liberation struggle if one helicopter can deliver a weapon like that. They were not even aware of the Canberra flying across – it is in fact an extremely quiet aircraft – and had assumed that the bombs had come from the same helicopter that dropped the smoke. 5 Squadron eventually keep a bombed-up aircraft and crew on standby at Sarum.

CHAPTER ELEVEN

Fireforce

The ascending whine of the siren has me instantly awake and rolling out of bed. Into shorts, bush shirt and veldskoens – no socks – a quick brush through the hair and grabbing my pistol belt, personal weapon and map case I am on my way to the ops room in less than half a minute. I see that the helicopters are already out of the revetments and the techs are moving out to them to get them teed up for starting. They are already fuelled to be at maximum all-up weight once the four man fireforce sticks are enplaned. The commando officer commanding is already in the ops room and he gives me a quick heads-up before the other pilots and stick commanders arrive for a formal brief for the forthcoming scene.

In this op area – we are positioned at Mtoko – the fireforce callouts are normally initiated as a result of Selous Scout OPs and pseudo teams, but for the last couple of weeks we have been getting grade one intelligence from a police ground coverage team who has successfully indicated the presence of terrorists several times, and we have had a series of contacts moving westwards across the area. Previously they have all been to our east, but the target gridref this morning is about twenty minutes flying time to our west. We have worked together for a while, so the briefing is quick but covers all the essentials of our airborne approach, and the intended initial run-in, where I want the Lynx positioned as we pull up over the target in the K-Car, and the Dakota lurking with the paratroops. Nearest local fuel supplies are marked out on the ops room maps and noted and the army indicate where their land tail will position on a road in the vicinity – this will have, as well as second wave reinforcing sticks, extra fuel and ammunition resupply for the helicopters – the Lynx will return here for fuel and re-arming. The various frequencies and fallbacks are confirmed and we outline a Plan A of likely stop positions in the event that everything works in our favour when we get there. Moving out to the aircraft, I notice the paratroops are almost kitted out and will be ready to embark very soon – they will take off after us and will arrive in the target area shortly after we do. The engines are already started and the sticks are already on board. I have the K-Car positioned behind the trooping helicopters so I arrive first, check my survival belt is in position, get my personal weapon in position lodged between my seat and the right-hand door and then pull the heavy two-piece flak jacket on, heave into the armoured seat and strap in. I start engaging the rotors once I am in the seat – keeping an eye on the stop clock as the fuel control lever has to be advanced at a particular speed – and noting that the temperatures are all in the green. The gunner has been monitoring the start from outside and checking for leaks and the like, the army commander has organised himself in his rearward-facing armoured seat on my left and we are ready to fly within five minutes of that abysmal wailing siren starting.

I can see the helicopters in front of me are all winding up and start taxiing forward, moving out past them to the left as I call the formation to check in, which they do in turn. As soon as I hear Yellow Four, the last, I call.

"One Delta Lima, Yellow formation, K-Car plus four is taxiing for immediate take-off on Zero Nine then departing low-level to the west." We are taking off in this direction in order to take advantage of any wind – the aircraft are heavy, it is starting to warm up and we are already using a lot of power.

The ops room acknowledges the call – it is not actually air traffic, but the call is basically letting all our aircraft know what is happening and is also a general warning for any aircraft in the vicinity of Mtoko to stay clear of the circuit as we have priority for our launch. After I pass Yellow lead, the trooping helicopters move into line ahead following us out. I check the runway and approaches are clear in both directions before moving onto Zero Nine, calling One Delta Lima that we are lifting and accelerate along the ground getting airborne and through transition then climbing away turning left, confirming to 1DL that we are airborne as a fireforce and estimate time on target in twenty-two minutes.

There is no high ground en route to help block out noise of our approach, so I keep our height down to about thirty feet over the bush. Yellow formation shakes out into a loose battle formation, which means it is a controllable entity, without having to concentrate on close formation. It also affords the opportunity for the best number of eyes on the ground we are covering, including the areas that we have just overflown, where many times alert gunners have seen gooks who have been in cover behind trees appear after we have passed.

The Lynx checks in airborne and confirms that he will be holding off to our right, and then the Dakota.

About ten minutes out from the target gridref I can see that it is a small rise, obviously not fifty feet high as it doesn't show on the map, where the contours are at fifty foot intervals. I point it out to Jerry Strong, the army commander. I brief the Lynx pilot that we will mark the target immediately with white smoke and he is to be on his perch for a frantan attack at that time. The gunner is standing by with the smoke generator as I angle to go slightly north of the centre of the rocky rise about a half mile in length.

"K-Car pulling up."

As we look down into the target area the smoke generator is thrown, and at the same time all three of us in the gunship see several denim-clad armed figures moving and trying to stay hidden.

"Open fire."

The gunner puts down three bursts onto the rock – that is going to get a lot of shrapnel flying around as the high-explosive rounds detonate.

"Echo Four, when you get the smoke visual you are clear in. Call 'in live.'"

"K-Car. Echo Four has your strike visual. Is that the target?"

"Affirmative."

"Echo Four is in live."

At that moment the thick white smoke starts to appear. It is slightly north of where the terrs are. I am aware of the Lynx starting his turn in.

"E4. When you have the smoke, add about ten, and put both frans straight on."

This isn't the SOP, but Jan Meine and I have been together many times and have devised this way of getting maximum firepower onto the target in the vital early stages of a contact, when the gooks are close together. The comment has been made a couple of times on airstrike reports that one canister should be dropped and then a correction given from that for a second attack. They don't seem to appreciate that we are not hitting a static target on the range, these guys move very fast and we have got to keep them in as small an area as possible. As long as we are confident we are talking about the same target, let's get it down quickly.

"Smoke visual. Adding ten."

We keep slamming twenty mill down into the figures skulking around until I see the Lynx stabilising in his dive and cease fire. The Lynx passes more or less under us and the two frans explode exactly where they were required. We pull in right behind him and start firing at individual targets.

The G-Cars have gone into a low orbit around us, maybe a quarter of a mile away. Jerry tells me more exact locations he would like his troops deplaned.

"Yellow lead, turn hard right."

I see one of the helicopters turning outwards from the orbit. To me, this is the quickest way to identify the helicopter I want, rather than fannying about getting rotating beacons turned on and the like.

"Yellow one, turn left."

"Roll out."

"Turn right. Roll out."

He follows my instructions, knowing that I will keep him clear of the other aircraft and not overflying the gook position.

"Standby."

"You are over your LZ now. Drop your troops in your own time."

Some people prefer to read the troopers right on to the drop position and tell them when to decelerate. For several reasons – mainly it means that your attention is away from the main target area and the pilot may assess that there is a better approach onto the specific LZ – I prefer the way I do it.

"Yellow two, turn hard right."

"Roll out."

We get three sticks on the ground, have a quick pause to drop a couple of targets snivelling in the fran attack area and then get Yellow 4's stick in place.

We want the paras dropped about three hundred yards to the north in one line in an east-west line. I brief Yellow one on what we want and leave him to organise this on a separate frequency with the Dakota. He will designate the actual DZ, give the Dak the local ground height and wind direction and they'll let us know when the drop has occurred. The plan is for them to come through the target area in an extended line from the north and either bring the enemy to contact during this sweep or drive them off the feature towards where the four stop groups have been positioned to deal with them. I send two of the helicopters off to the land tail to refuel, keeping one handy in case we need a casevac or need to reposition a stick.

The paradrop is carried out and the sweep gets organised. I brief one of the refuelled guys to take over top cover and push off to get refuelled. I want to be back overhead before the sweep gets onto the target in order to be available for close support for the ground troops. Jerry decides he can stay with us rather than get transferred into one of the G-Cars – the enemy don't seem inclined to move off from their rocks – they have seen the troops being positioned, and either tactically or more likely due to lack of ideas, have decided to defend there as the sweep approaches. The Dakota, of course, has repositioned at Mtoko after the drop and we send the Lynx off to rearm with a couple of frans and refuel as well, but to return asap.

It takes about half an hour before we are back overhead and Yellow three, who has been keeping control of the scene, says that there has been some movement on the feature but nobody appears to have made a break off it. We send him and Yellow lead off to refuel and call two and four into a low orbit to help contain the group in the killing ground. The centre of the para sweep has now reached the edge of the rocks and Jerry starts to control their assault – at this stage ensuring that the dressing remains and fire groups are not losing direction and firing into each other. Although the paras are in an extended sweep line, they fight in their classic four man sticks within that, each having its own radio comms, one MAG gunner and three riflemen. As a stick makes contact, the line halts whilst the stick deploys itself to deal with the threat and are ready to continue. Now and again an adjacent stick will assist, if required, with fire support. There are a few contacts as the sweep approaches the area of the fran strike. Twice we are asked to put in twenty mill onto positions indicated either by description of the stick commander on the ground or by firing a mini flare onto the troublesome place.

Moving through the area of the fran strike, several bodies are found. The RLI don't have to be reminded not to trust these 'bodies', they always put a double-tap into them before approaching, and are ultra-careful before moving them. When we are working with less experienced battalions, we always warn them of the possibility of corpses suddenly coming alive – perhaps mortally wounded and having their last hurrah – and dying terrorists booby-trapping their own bodies by lying on top of a primed grenade that will explode as they are moved.

On this occasion we take no casualties, and the body-count plus two wounded prisoners adds up to the intelligence we had of the group size. Jerry asks if we can land so he can brief his stick commanders on the ground and I need a pee anyway so we land away from the rocks – just in case there any bad guys still lurking. As the soldiers are bringing in the bodies to be taken out – the G-Cars will uplift them to the land tail – I am intrigued to see that many have weapons with 'four by two' cleaning cloth still in the muzzle – they haven't even fired their weapons.

The uplift of the first wave and paras is organised, the bodies, weapons and recovered parachutes will be returned with the second wave troops in the land tail, and we ease back to Mtoko. I have an hour before the G-Cars will all be back and re-armed and refuelled, so I get the airstrike signal away to headquarters and start writing the report that will follow. As we have not used a lot of ordnance on this occasion – although a lot of the dead have horrendous shrapnel wounds, a lot of the damage has been caused by rock splinters – I overstate the number of rounds we have fired. The total is not large enough to evoke any comment from those neddies who get concerned about using ammunition, but gives me some addition in a notional pool of ammunition that I can draw from when we do use an excess of twenty mill, to keep the reported expenditure down. We have specific orders not to use the cannon to provide clearing fire into thick bush for advancing troops, but I have no problem doing that if the guys on the ground want it. It's just the double-bookkeeping that you have to keep on top of.

On one of my early fireforce actions we were being led by a South African pilot on attachment. We had trackers down and ahead of them we could easily see where the terrs had made their way through tall grass. The tracks went into a patch of trees and bush and the troops were being positioned as stop groups around this vegetation with two sticks linking up to sweep into it. They requested some flushing fire to be directed into the area, and some 7.62 was put down. The assaulting sticks moved up close to the suspect area and at very close range the terrs opened up – presumably they had watched the deployments around them and realised that this was going to be their last stand. The firefight stabilised and a voice came on saying that they had three casualties, one of whom was the senior guy on the ground, Captain Pitch, who had been shot through the neck and needed immediate casevac. They had a problem in that although they were in a donga that gave them cover, as soon as they tried to extricate him they were getting a severe snottie from the gooks. They were seriously worried about the amount of blood the casualty was losing and reckoned he had to be got out immediately as it appeared to be arterial and they were having difficulties applying pressure to stop it. The K-Car pilot can't seem to get a grip and he is having a problem trying to converse in English and keeps reverting to Afrikaans. I offer to land for an immediate casevcac and am told to go ahead and try. I brief the stick on the ground that I will land alongside them in the donga and they are to immediately load the casualty into the right-hand side of the cabin; my gunner will be firing his MAG out of the left whilst we are on the ground. Immediately prior to our arriving I am getting the fixed wing to throw his frans right onto the area just to our left. The pilot is Cocky Beneke in a Provost. Although the safety distances are way out, this is the only way I reckon we can do this, and Cocky's weapons deliveries are normally very accurate. We co-ordinate our run in with his turning in live, but miscalculate slightly and land in the donga as he is still in the dive. The gooks have just realised what is happening and start firing but it is mostly going over our top. The gunner has the MAG going on more or less continuously and I suppose about two seconds go by when there is a massive double explosion right next to us and an enormous fireball as Cocky's two frantans explode – the heat is incredible. The casualty is bundled on and we lift out in double quick time. I call Darwin to have the doctor meet the aircraft as we land – we will be there in ten minutes. The tech has got another drip into the casualty, the one the troops had put in on the ground having come off in getting him on board. The doctor duly meets us and starts immediately cutting into the patient's neck and quickly gets the blood flow slowed by putting some clamps on the artery. He indicates that he wants to get the guy to Bindura hospital, and asks if I can organise this over the radio. It will mean getting Cocky back in the Provost so that he can change aircraft to the Trojan. I tell the doctor that we will go straight

down in the helicopter and call for an immediate lift and tell
ops what we are doing. The flight takes about twenty minutes
and the doctor is working the whole time doing what, to me,
looks like some pretty extensive surgery. Bindura hospital has
been pre-warned and is very efficient as a team meets us on
their pad and transfer the guy onto a wheeled trolley and away
in quick time. As the doctor leaves us, I ask if he wants to go
straight into Andrew Fleming, but he thinks they have got the
chap stabilised and they've got adequate facilities here, so we
get some fuel topped up and get back to Darwin. We are told in
the evening that the exercise had been a success and the chap
is alive and well.

There is big discussion as to whether the bush should
have been given a good working over with twenty mill or
even frantan before the troops were tasked to go in there. It is
difficult to have any impact on the official line as everybody is
cock a hoop that we have wiped the small group out without
expending a lot of ammunition and without anyone being killed
on our side. The good vibes means that the circumstances of
the casevac are quietly brushed aside. Had things turned out
differently there would have been an awful lot of sucking of
breath and quoting of weapons safety distances. I seriously
wonder what is going on in some of these neddies' heads. Do
they really not understand that we are not on a practice range
and the troops are fighting at distances of maybe ten yards in
thick bush?

I resolve to never concern myself about cost of ammunition
when the guys on the ground need to have covering fire. It is a
continuing nag from headquarters throughout the war. Later,
we get signals at the fireforces stating that 'the intention is not
to influence commanders' operational decisions' and then
laying out the respective costs of the various air ordnance.
Most expensive are the 30mm rounds for the Hunter, followed

by the 20mm for our K-Car cannons. We are free to use as much 7.62 or .303 as we like. Trouble is, until we eventually get a four gun .303 fit, you can't get it down in a sufficiently concentrated amount to have any real effect. In all fairness, when that fit comes in it is pretty effective – the concentration of fire is not far off that of the famed revolving mini guns of the Americans. But that is a couple of years ahead.

Very sadly, the end of the story changes. Len Pitch is transferred by ambulance from Bindura to Salisbury for ongoing treatment. About halfway there he suffers an aneurism. It is fatal.

Back at Mtoko, I get the airstrike report finished soon after the other helicopters return. If you don't get this stuff out of the way, it mounts up very quickly. If you go through a period of having three or four contacts a day for a day or so you genuinely can't remember them as different punch-ups and they seem to coalesce into one continuous never-ending battle.

The fireforce is redeployed to Mount Darwin. We have a couple of busy days and there is a 'no moon' night so all the aircrew are stood down for the night, albeit with the standby casevac crew still available in case of dire need.

The RLI commanding officer, Colonel Peter Rich, calls for me in the ops room at about 23:00. A farm is being attacked between us and Bindura. The gooks are inside the security fence, the house has been hit with at least three RPGs, the farmer has been killed and the wife is there with two very young children and armed with a double-barrelled shotgun. The gooks are in the garden, but have satisfied themselves so far with shooting at the house rather than assaulting it. It is going to take the best part of an hour for ground troops to get there by road –

is there any possibility we can fly the fireforce there? We are airborne five minutes later. It is as black as a witch's tit, and to complicate matters there are no direct comms. The only link is via the agri-alert system. However, we establish some contact via the ops room, relaying to the nearest police unit who then relay to the farm.

I have all the aircraft turn their rotating beacons on – we don't need a midair, that's for sure – and then get the message over for the woman to keep the lights off until I call for them in about ten minutes' time, when she is to turn them all on and then all off again ten seconds later. She and the children are then to get in as much cover inside the house as they can, as my plan is to slam down as much twenty mill all around and as close to the house as I can and there is liable to be shrapnel, ricochets and stray bullets flying around. The G-Cars are to hold off firing unless they positively have targets visual, as they will be in a left-hand orbit with the house nominally in the centre and I don't want streams of machine gun fire going in that direction. The formation has strung out to give everybody manoeuvring room, and I brief them that I will try and locate a LZ close to the security fence where they are to offload their troops one aircraft at a time and then set up an orbit about a half mile off using the house as the focus. They are not to be frightened of using the landing lights and to keep their eyes skinned for wires and the like lurking in the vicinity. I get each pilot to confirm that he is fully conversant with the plan.

As the dead reckoning time is approaching, I call for the house lights and shortly afterwards they come on almost on the nose, and as they go off we are just about there, roll into a firing orbit and put in three orbits' worth of fairly continuous fire around the farm.

There is an area close by the security fence which looks big enough for the formation to have landed, but I stay with the original plan and the aircraft do a text book deplaning of their troops and move off into an enveloping orbit. The first stick advance through the fence, clear the garden and get into the house. The family are safe.

The other sticks are consolidated and start an immediate follow up. There are no bodies, but discarded equipment and weapons, and they are soon on blood spoor. However, we decide to belay any serious follow up until first light, by which time we will have dedicated trackers and have got ourselves reorganised. I have landed on the lawn and we meet the wife and her two children. She fills us in with the details.

The dogs had started barking and the farmer went onto the verandah with his FN, unfortunately turning the lights on. He was taken out by a fusillade of small arms fire immediately and RPGs were fired at the building. One of them went through the children's bedroom, but caused only material damage. She had the sense to douse all the house and verandah lights and grabbed the only other weapon, a double-barrelled shotgun, with just two rounds of ammunition. Seeing movement across the lawn as the terrorists are approaching the house, she fires one barrel and they go to ground, from which they don't move until the helicopters arrive. I ask what the plan was with her remaining shotgun round and she calmly tells me that it would have taken out the first man who appeared over the verandah.

The medic yells that the farmer is still alive and starts to arrange a drip and deal with the gunshot wounds. As he is being stabilised and cocooned on a stretcher, a G-Car is detailed off to casevac him to Bindura hospital. The wife wants to go with him, but with the stretcher and a medic in the back of the aircraft there isn't really room, certainly not with two toddlers as well, so I detail off one of the other two G-Cars to get her and the children – having got them all wrapped up warmly and securely strapped in – in fireforce duties we have the seat straps stowed away as they are never used – and send him off as well, with orders to stay there for the night and we'll contact him in the morning with instructions on rejoining us.

The troops are left at the farm, where they will be joined during the night by trackers and organise a follow up in the light, and I take the helicopters back to Darwin, have a bacon sarnie and coffee as I send an airstrike signal prior to falling into bed.

Peter Rich calls me to the ops room first thing in the morning and shows me a signal.

I have been invited to send my 'reasons in writing' to explain 1) why I took helicopters on a moonless night 2) why I wasted fifty-odd rounds of 20mm ammunition on a non-visual target – with no resulting kills (there is the usual comment about using 7.62 for flushing fire) and 3) authorised a helicopter flight to carry three civilians, also at night.

He then tells me that he is dealing with it and shows his reply. Over coffee I persuade him to make one addition – state that it wasn't flushing fire, it was a demonstration of firepower before landing in a proven hostile environment – we may as well get the terminology correct. The episode is brushed aside.

★

We have been living under canvas on a hilltop at Mudzi with an RAR fireforce. We have had only one contact with two, who were killed, otherwise it has been a bit 'Out of Africa', with hot baths in a tin tub watching the sunset. The company is being repositioned by road to Mtoko, but we take the first wave troops by air. As we land at Mtoko we are whisked to the ops room and briefed on a Selous Scouts scene, where an OP has a camp visual. The RAR major radios his land tail and orders them to prepare a second wave on the road and we get airborne. We have a South African driving the K-Car and he elects to fly a roundabout route to provide noise cover as we approach the target. As we come out of the hills we fly into a wide valley which is relatively vegetation-free. The K-Car is having a heated radio exchange with the OP, who is obviously an African and is trying to tell him he is going to the wrong gridref. Unfortunately, he is keeping his Prestel switch depressed and nobody else can transmit. We can see the target, and the troops in my aircraft get terrs visual and we commence firing. They are on a wooded hillock and there is clear ground all around. Mike Upton is firing well with the MAG, but there is a lot of accurate small arms fire directed at us, some of which is hitting. We have two firing orbits before the OP is able to tell the K-Car that the other helicopters are in contact. He comes over and fires one burst before withdrawing.

"I've been hit. The major's been hit."

He moves off, and we continue the contact, but we are taking some punishment; there are many red lights coming up on the instrument panel, including the big red main gearbox warning, which means the oil is gone and you are to get on the ground within about thirty seconds. The aircraft is already in manual – the hydraulics have been disabled – and then the gun belt is hit and severed and our gun disabled. I disengage and tell Mike to tell the troops we are forced landing and to prepare for a quick debus as we will be right in the contact area.

We arrive in a semi-controlled heap about half a click from the camp and the RAR troops are out and in a defensive circle around the aircraft as I get the engine shut down and the blades stopped. Mike has a bit of trouble disentangling himself from his monkey belt but we get ourselves sorted out – or relatively. Mike has previously been in the RLI and is often berating me to carry an FN as my personal weapon rather than the sub-machine gun. His FN had broken open at the stock during our deplaning and all the working parts had slid out. He has desperately tried to reassemble them, but obviously some of the springs had gone awol and he now has what amounts to an expensive club for defence.

"Sir, sir, give me your weapon."

I reply with a short enquiry as to whether he enjoys sex and travel, but then somewhat reluctantly pass over my pistol. He suggests I take off my flying gloves that are white, or whitish, but I point out that he has a mop of absolutely blonde hair that is going to attract more attention than my gungy gloves. We join up with the RAR stick, but they are sweeping into the camp area, which is an appalling idea. We quickly get into a couple of short-range contacts – I am shocked when two terrs surrender themselves after a lot of shouting in Shona between themselves and our soldiers and appear out of a crack in the ground some ten feet in front of us. Shortly afterwards, Dick Paxton lands a G-Car close to us and we are despatched with the two prisoners under guard. Dick has arrived with the Darwin fireforce; he landed as he'd seen the disabled helicopter on the ground and his gunner had recognised Mufti's blonde hair, so maybe it was some use after all.

The K-Car had been hit immediately on arriving at the contact, and unfortunately the army commander, Mike Ainslie, had been killed by the only two bullets that hit the aircraft.

★

Two days later, with no available gunship, I lead three G-Cars onto another sighting and we get straight into contact – a big snottie of small arms hits the cockpit as we arrive at low-level. My left arm is thrown off the collective, it feels like a massive cane stroke on my hand and there is a lot of blood dripping through my glove. The group is three, and we get them caught in the crossfire of all three aircraft in the centre of a tight orbit and are able to drop all three before landing our soldiers. There is a moment when we have another guy visual. There are three lines of tracer reaching out towards him but he is walking along shaking his head as though there are a swarm of bees around him. I call a ceasefire – he is obviously unaware of what is happening or is Mr Cool strolling away from the contact zone and deserves to get away. I hand over control and start back for Mtoko handling the controls very carefully – there is a big hole in the floor where we have been hit. Under there is where the main control rods are located, and losing any one of them would really spoil our day. It is why I have discarded the idea of attempting a hover landing in the bush as there would have to be a lot of moving, and hence strain, on the linkages. On the way back, Mike is worried about the blood loss – I tell him to get himself alongside me and to be prepared to assist me on the collective as the left arm is starting to seize up – and inform Mtoko of the situation, to make sure I am clear to a rolling landing on the runway and to have the fire truck and an ambulance on hand.

The landing goes off without any drama, but I am in the hospital having shrapnel picked out of my hand and arm and various leakages being sutured when Mufti comes in holding one of the control rods he has removed. It has had a round go through it which was obviously tumbling – the crack has gone around over four hundred degrees around the tube, but the two ends didn't join up and there was a sliver of metal holding the tube together. Luckily, he has brought a cold bottle of beer with him.

★

We have had a punch-up east of Darwin in the Rutenga area. We are close to closing up when a callsign on the ground alerts us to a gook snivelling away through the cultivated fields to the bush. Greg Todd is in the other gunship and we both get visual with this guy who is in the corner of the last cleared field before he will be in the bush. We both get low overhead him and open up, which gets him moving. A field obviously has a short side and a long side, but with both aircraft sending streams of 20mm at him this guy starts to run diagonally across the field. He is armed with an RPD and is running in a series of circles firing at us – and as it happens, hitting both aircraft. The ground is erupting around him as he makes it almost all the way across the field. Just before reaching the diagonally opposite corner he runs out of ammunition. He stops dead, and both streams of fire overshoot him. I watch him hold the weapon out horizontally and look at it with disgust before throwing it down and then he strolls off the field of battle and disappears into the thick bush.

With this display of aplomb, he deserves to survive, but sadly, when the troops finally sweep through that area, they find his body just within the bush and it is riddled with shrapnel.

CHAPTER TWELVE

Victoria Falls

I am sent on a 'rest' tour for two weeks to Wankie in the north-west of the country. The air staff have been forced to realise that a series of minor handling accidents and an increase in bizarre and unreasonable behaviour by deployed crews is at least in part due to the extreme strain that they are operating under. A couple of staff officers have been deployed to visit all the forward airfields under some cover pretext, with the actual mission of observing the crews and reporting back. Of course, their cover is blown before they start and everybody has a great time thinking up wheezes that will be reported in the copious notes they are taking.

The clincher for getting everybody a break off operations comes paradoxically from their visit to Wankie, where Dick Paxton and Luigi Mantovani are temporarily based. They are, of course, pre-warned of the impending visit. Having parked their Cessna, the wing commanders introduce themselves to the ops staff and enquire on the whereabouts of the chopper crews. Luigi, who is one of the pilots, but whom they don't recognise dressed in casual bush attire, directs them to the small pond in the camp area, where they find Paxton resplendent in top hat, shorts and T-shirt squatting by the pond with a fishing pole. They wander up and engage him in conversation.

"Caught anything, Dick?"

"No sir. Of course not, there's no bait on my hook."

There is an exchange of knowing looks and a furtive scribble, just before the camp broadcast system opens up with Luigi intoning:

"Paxton's lost his marbles. Paxton's lost his marbles."

They cut their visit short.

★

Luigi has just recovered from a broken nose. Funnily enough, it has not been administered by Pete McCabe, whom he nearly killed by taxiing into a road sign whilst landing on a road in the Inyanga area, where the refuelling point had been established in an operation. The balance weights in the tips of the blades detach and some strike Pete in the chest at several hundred miles an hour. He is knocked flat, but is luckily saved from other than serious bruising by his flak vest. Back in his scratcher late one night at Grand Reef, Luigi is awoken by the rattle of machine gun fire followed by a tremendous crash through the window and something heavy landing on his nose and rolling on to his chest. He is terrified to move, convinced the camp is under attack and a mortar shell is lying on his chest and hasn't exploded.

It is, in fact, a lump of rock. The Dakota pilots are returning from a drinking match with the Browns and decide it will be a good idea to wake everybody up by throwing gravel on the corrugated iron roofs. The rock has come from the venerable 'Prof' Christie, who has been flying since about the time Pontius was a Pilate, and does his call-up in between his real job as Dean of Law at the university. His aim, or perhaps his strength, isn't as good as it used to be.

After his war experiences and wounds, Mantos gives up flying and becomes a greengrocer.

★

I've been to Wankie once before, but this is Doris' first visit, so he has never met Harvey, the resident hornbill. Harvey struts around the camp as befits his self-imposed rank of sergeant-major, and is understandably miffed when Doris doesn't recognise his position and perceives him as a resident plaything for him to chase. Ground hornbills are a bit like pilots a year or so out of training – they don't like getting airborne more often than is absolutely necessary to draw their flying pay. To escape this great hairy beast galumphing around, however, Harvey puts in more flying time than he has in the last year and takes to strutting around on the ops room roof, with the odd sortie onto one of the rotor blades and an occasional trip to the ground to spear a snack, after a good look around to make sure the coast is clear. He re-establishes authority on the fourth day. Doris is surprised to see him perched by the pond and breaks into a half-hearted trot, knowing Harvey is not going to play, and will quickly flap off.

But Harvey shows no sign of moving and the dog speeds up. Eventually, as Doris is getting really close, Harvey languidly gets airborne, but instead of climbing fast for the roof he stays low and slow, positioning himself tantalisingly out of reach a little above Doris' nose and a yard or so in front and leads him across the camp. Doris has to raise his nose to keep his quarry visual from under his shaggy brows, so the low wall across the grassy area is out of his vision. The bird skims over the wall, but of course it takes Doris' legs out from under him and he ends up in a great tumbling mass of hair and dust. Harvey lands and struts triumphantly past, not too close, and from then on they keep their distance from each other, but the sergeant-major resumes his strutting on the ground, rather than the sulking presence on the roof of the last few days.

★

The last time I was here, it was one of my early deployments since joining the squadron and I had an unusually busy and varied time. Gordon Wright was the FAF Commander at the time, and I'm quite glad he's not here as he has probably not forgiven me for my performance – or lack of it – in a cricket match against the local police. It is a twenty-over affair where everybody has to bowl two overs. My twelve balls are all sent for boundaries, and as one of our players can't bowl, the police get to choose two of us to bowl another over each. Of course one of their choices is me, and I get whacked for another sixteen off four balls, but inexplicably get two wickets also – I think the batsmen had just got tired arm muscles from slogging me all over the ground. Gordon takes his cricket seriously and is mightily unpleased that my figures read two for sixty-four. We go in to bat, and largely due to his prowess with the bat we have reached the position where we are three runs short of victory with four balls to go in the over before last. The problem is that Gordon is at the wrong end and probably now regrets demoting me to last man in, as by getting rid of me earlier there would have been a more reliable watchman to see out the over and give him the last six balls to knock off the required runs. I waddle out from the pavilion, and as is custom, he meets me and gives me a briefing on my way to the crease. I am just to keep a straight bat and block the four balls so that we get into the last over, not to wave my bat around at any point as the bowler is very, very fast and the slightest nick will go straight to the slips.

I get into position and go through the rituals of asking for 'middle and leg', scraping the ground with the bat, holding it aloft and looking around at the fielding set up, adjusting my box and finally putting bat to ground to signal that I am ready, and look up for the bowler. Where the hell is he?

Then I catch some movement, and there is a whirling dervish accelerating from some point on the horizon at a phenomenal rate – what's he doing on the pitch? As he closes with the opposite wicket I realise this is the bowler. I never see the ball but feel the disturbed airflow and hear a whirr as it passes close to my ear – this is long before the days of helmets.

I do at least see the next two balls, but they are already passed before I get the bat into line, and they cross my wicket dangerously close. Gordon is visibly agitated at the other end and obviously praying to some deity that I will survive the last missile. It pitches well in front but doesn't take the line of the other three and cuts in viciously towards me at just about the height of my favourite sporting tackle. I change my grip on the bat and in a purely protective measure execute what would nowadays be called a reverse sweep – it was nothing of the sort, it was a pure reflexive defence, and not the sort of stroke anybody would employ against a fast inswinger. Which is probably why it catches everybody off guard, loops over third man and takes one bounce on its way to the boundary. We've won. And why use skill when you can rely on luck? The Rhodesians, however, treat sport like a sacred religion rather than an activity you undertake to fill in the time between the bar shutting and re-opening, and I'm left in the corner wondering if I've trodden in something nasty. What the hell, we won – I go to have a drink with the police team, but their fast bowler is mightily hacked off also as I've ruined his figures. Good God, what's the matter with these people? He should look at my bowling average.

I get tasked to go up towards Victoria Falls to assist in a SAS cross-Zambezi deployment. I ask if I can night-stop in Vic Falls. Gordon agrees, to the surprise of Tweedy Reid-Daly, but it isn't because he wants to assist in my tourism activities: there's another cricket match coming up and he wants me as far from the vicinity as possible. As they also want to be deployed at last light it means we can justify a short night hop into the police LZ at the Falls, rather than a flog back to FAF 1.

We RV with the SAS guys and I am introduced to their commander – a fearsome little man, Brian Robinson – and the patrol commander, Tim Callow, who is about seven feet tall and very laid back. There seems to be some bad feeling between the two of them, and Tim tells me later that it is because the previous night, when they had tried to deploy across by boat, he'd dropped one of the unit's two night vision sights into the river. The mighty Zambezi is a roaring torrent through the gorges here; I am surprised they would have even attempted a water crossing as I look down when we cross it a few minutes later. I know how he feels; the atmosphere is rather like making a pillock of yourself at cricket, but it doesn't seem appropriate to make that comparison. These guys are rubbing black into their faces, priming grenades and trying to fit their knives between their lips.

We're quite heavy and Tweedy is worried that we won't have enough power to get out of the LZ, but I've noticed a hole in the tall trees and do a right-hand climbing orbit of the clearing and as we arrive just under the hole push in some left yaw pedal, which has the dual effects of giving a little extra power to bring us level with the hole and turning the nose left to get through it at the same time. It's the first time I've managed to impress one of the squadron techs; up until now they've been drawing straws to determine the loser, who will fly with me.

He's even more impressed a while later when, after landing at the police LZ, I persuade the police to lend us a Land Rover and we go and book into a local hotel. He tells me that it is normal practice to roll out sleeping bags on the verandah of the police station, and he's a little worried about how we're going to settle the bill, but the reception staff are quite happy with my instructions to send the bill to Air Force Headquarters at Causeway, Salisbury. Aside from anything else – why sleep on the floor when there is a perfectly good bed nearby? – I want to ensure I am not sharing the same sleeping space as Tweedy. A few weeks back, we had flown over from Mutawatawa with the rest of our fireforce to celebrate the opening of the new pub at Mtoko. Tweedy stumbled into the room we were all crashing out in about an hour after everybody else had gone to bed. He was totally arse-holed and kept trying to climb on to my stretcher, which he was convinced was his. In the end I told him just to lie still and shut up and he could stay. Within ten seconds he was snoring like a hippopotamus – but at least he stayed still.

We have a quick shower and get stuck into the time-proved routine of a run ashore – a few wets in the town bars, and the desperate search for some stray 'white panty'. It rarely works like that of course; you normally end up penniless, drunk and having lost your coat somewhere. For once, however, circumstances fall into line; we end up at the new luxury hotel up the Zambezi a little, the 'Elephant Hills' – where Richard Burton and Elizabeth Taylor have just spent a highly publicised visit – which has a casino. I have a little luck at the tables, and a little more when I get into conversation with one of the off-duty croupiers who has recently been found surplus to requirements by her boyfriend.

She has some point to prove, and I am pretty shattered by the time we get airborne next morning, so we do a bit of IFR flying back to Wankie – as in 'I follow the railway'. Unlike at cricket, I am invited back to play again when I have a break.

★

We get involved in a night casevac into the game park to uplift a game ranger who has been run over by a buffalo. Whilst waiting at the main airport to transfer him into a fixed-wing I ask him what happened. He is badly battered and has broken legs, arms and ribs, but is quite lucid. He tells me the animal charged and he got all five shots of his rifle into its head, before it was ten yards away. He'd killed it, but unfortunately the buff didn't realise that and ran over him before dropping dead about twenty yards the other side.

By the time the extraction of Tim Callow is due, I have a different gunner. The extraction, which is only a short hop over the river and back, is fine, but then we are called to go to the Fall's police LZ. After we land, the member-in-charge tells me that a woman has tried to commit suicide by jumping into the gorge. Unlike a lot of similar locations – if anything can be thought of as similar to the spectacular Victoria Falls – there is no protective fencing at the gorges, but there is in fact a very low incidence of attempted suicides. This woman's body is visible on a rock in the gorge and there is some doubt as to whether she is still alive or not – can we get in there with the helicopter and try to retrieve the casualty?

I go and look at it and we have two attempts at getting in. Perhaps unsurprisingly, the turbulence is unbelievable, both when we try and get in from above and then try and approach low-level up through the lower gorges. We go back and land and I apologise but I am not going to risk going in for what is probably a body anyway. Dick Paxton and his gunner have recently been awarded MFCs for recovering a body under World's View a few months back. The chap was a hang gliding enthusiast who an hour before had asked Dick's advice on the viability of flying off the brick. He'd been told it was an inherently stupid idea due to the turbulence and backdrafts, but had a go anyway with the fatal result, and the crew had

retrieved the remains on the same basis: he might just be alive
– he wasn't. Our suicide's body is washed downstream a day
later and recovered – she was certainly dead by then.

We refuel, and I fly over to the 'Elephant Hills' and, to JB's
mystification, land in the car park. The manager and staff rush
out and after we've shut down ask worriedly what is wrong.
I explain that I am just calling in to arrange some R and R
with Rosa, one of his croupiers. He's terribly sorry, they've just
sent her over to Kariba on relief, she hadn't said anything. It
was a casual arrangement, it's no big deal. He is still very sorry
and invites us for lunch – which is superb – and a tour of the
hotel, which is impressive. There are only twelve suites, and it
is apparent there is a very low occupancy.

Having ascertained that I am down the way at Wankie and
am due my R and R in a few days, he invites both of us to
come and stay. Thanks very much, but a month's pay would just
about cover twenty-four hours.

"My dear chaps. As our guests. As our guests."

John can't arrange his diary and is really pissed off, but
I practically trip over my tongue accepting. On returning to
the FAF I call Griff, the squadron commander, and explain
I'd like to spend my days off here rather than catching the
Dakota back to Salisbury. He agrees that is fine, on the
proviso that I'm back on duty on the required day under my
own steam.

Changeover day comes, and having handed over I get a lift
down to the local railway siding. I've arranged a lift up to
Victoria Falls with a chap I met at the Colliery Club, and travel
the miles on the footplate of a Garrett pulling a long goods train
– probably the first visitor to the Elephant Hills Country Club,

as it was then called, to arrive by train, and almost certainly the only one ever to arrive on a freight train.

The Country Club was sadly burnt down during the war, and not even deliberately. A stray rocket fired during an attack from Zambia overshot the town and set light to the thatch with catastrophic consequences. The complex was rebuilt, but under the auspices of a completely different strategy aimed at mass tourism rather than the exclusive market.

My stay is predictably incredible. The service is discreet and unfaultable, the golf course, designed by Gary Player, has wildlife casually strolling across the fairways and its own rules on local hazards such as crocodiles in the water traps and elephants on the approach, and the food is sumptuous.

Despite my protestations, the manager insists on signing off dinner with him and his wife the first two nights. I arrive back at the hotel fairly late in the afternoon on the third day, having been out walking through the bush, and call my host to invite him to dinner.

"Mike, where have you been? We've been trying to get you all afternoon."

He cuts through my explanation, and asks if I can be ready for dinner in half an hour.

Even I am embarrassed now, and decline the invitation, but he cuts through again, insists that I will be helping him out, he'll be sending a dinner jacket around and to meet him for drinks in thirty minutes when he'll explain the panic to me.

Oh well, if it's in the line of duty. I get scrubbed up and present myself on parade, where he explains that Southern Suns, the hotel owners, and Air Rhodesia are launching a joint marketing drive and he and his wife have to entertain the heavies and their wives from both companies at dinner and après tonight. They have discovered there is an unaccompanied female with the visitors, and that is my task – to keep her out of the main conversation.

Oh God. I've been on these blind date missions before – it is normally somebody's grandmother, or even worse, the chubby sister with a good sense of humour or the drippy one who can cook for Africa, even though her glasses steam up, who never seems to meet a 'suitable' man. The fact of the matter is there is no such thing as a free lunch, and I have a few markers to cancel out here.

I've obviously done something right in the eyes of the gods – the visitors arrive for drinks and in the introductions I discover my mission for the evening, who is stunningly beautiful and is either Miss Rhodesia or Miss Flame Lily or something. She is absolutely fabulous company and we have a great time over dinner. My companion on the other side is Mrs Travers, who is also charming, and having enquired who I am, how I got to be at this table and my plans for getting back to Salisbury, will not countenance that and persuades her husband to arrange passage on Air Rhodesia.

It turns out that one of the purposes of the evening is to take some photographs for new publicity brochures, so there are a couple of snappers hovering continuously around. We do some shots on various balconies and then move to the casino, where we are given a bunch of chips and told to play at various tables but to bet biggish stacks. It is made quite plain that they are nominal values, we're not going to receive any payout, and perhaps for that reason we win quite significantly more often than not. However, the photographers are not getting the shots they want and we are told to wait at a spare table whilst they have a huddle to discuss the next move. Whilst sitting around with all these piles of chips, I introduce them to 'matches', and we have a great time for twenty minutes betting fortunes on the number of matches being concealed in the group's collective hands. Unobserved, the scene is photographed from several angles, and these shots of half a dozen laughing people around a green baize table with stacks of gambling chips are the ones used in the brochures – but the game of 'matches' isn't mentioned as one of the attractions. The party breaks up and the couples disperse.

There are few more romantic ambiences than sipping champagne on a balcony under the panoramic black and starlit African night sky, with the raw sounds of the African bush as background, and she accepts my offer of an escort back to her room. We seem to be really comfortable in each other's company. Before I can even make pathetic offers of excuses to move further, I am very charmingly, discreetly but firmly finessed, and it is plain I am not being invited in. We kiss. It starts to linger, but it is most likely my imagination. And she is gone. For once, the rejection doesn't feel as though I've been kneed in the nuts. For once, I haven't been.

★

Coincidentally, I am here at Wankie with JB again. We do no flying for a week, apart from an air test, which is really an excuse to see if there are any bikinis lying around the pool at the local club. There is one scheduled task coming up, a radio relay station crew change and resupply.

The night before, for no particular reason, JB and I hang one on in the FAF bar. We get involved in a game of liar dice with the national service airfield guards. This eventually turns into a game of 'seven, fourteen and twenty-one', an ace-driven drinking game, where the thrower of the seventh ace nominates a drink, the fourteenth pays for it and the twenty-first drinks it. Somebody else can work out the various probabilities, but with the right number of players you can get into a cycle where the same player hits a real losing streak. One of the other rules is that the same mix of two drinks cannot be nominated twice, so the cocktails become more and more bizarre. One of the TFs gets into the losing cycle, and by the time the game has progressed to one, two, three is getting into a serious state – he has two fast, consecutive losses and then a third, which is a tot of angostura bitters and a tot of anti-malaria tablets. Thankfully, he collapses before finishing the last concoction.

None of us is entirely sober, and as the session breaks up and as JB, who is a very big man, staggers out of the wooden building he lurches into the door frame and the whole end of the building becomes skewed at an angle, like the aftermath of an earthquake.

We arrive at the aircraft the following morning, where the changeover relay crew already have their stores on board and are waiting. They have been regaled with stories of the aircrew's involvement in the previous night's activities and try not to appear too discomfited when JB and I drift out taking sips from a J&B whiskey bottle. John tells them to mount up and hops into the pilot's seat, straps in and gets the motor going whilst I wander around tapping things with a screwdriver, which is what techs seem to do during a start, and clamber behind the guns – we have of course swapped overalls, and the whiskey is cold tea. John leans back and says that he is going to cancel the flight as he feels too ill to fly. We take a couple more slugs and have a discussion about the flight – the soldiers are trying to look unconcerned, but are paying pretty close attention, particularly when I goad him:

"Jesus, sir, these things are a piece of piss to fly, even I can do it."

This theme continues for a bit, and of course we eventually change seats – the troops are really paying attention now. We get the rotors in motion.

"If you can taxi it to the runway, I'll take over and we'll do the trip," from John. All this is being carried out of course, not by intercom, but shouting over the troops' heads.

We lurch and zig-zag out to the runway. I turn to deliberately look at JB, whilst easing the cyclic forward and taking in the collective, so it looks as though we get airborne accidentally. The hands start tightening on the strap-hangs. We do a 360 yaw pedal turn whilst moving uncertainly forward and upwards. The knuckles are getting very white. John is screaming out instructions on how to get the nose pointing in the direction we want to go and keeping wings level, and at one point unstraps and starts to clamber forward to 'change seats'. I knock off a couple of circuit breakers for unessential services, and we get a couple of amber warning lights up on the panel and a red 'generator out' light. I spend a lot of time looking backwards, whilst JB is instructing me on how to deal with these, and I can see the stick leader's eyes getting wider and wider – his hands are now in rigor mortis – as we are flying directly into the side of a mountain. Just as his mouth starts to articulate a scream, I look forward, haul the nose back and do a cyclic climb, levelling the nose to land in one movement on the mountain LZ; I have of course known exactly where we were the whole time. There is the fastest debus ever, and having got the other team onboard we lift, get a bit of altitude and airspeed and come back for a very fast and low beat-up, during which we drop the 'whiskey', pull a couple of torque turns in a mini air display and transit away to a stream of invective over the radio.

We think it is funny anyway.

I am on my four days off from the bush, but the boss has asked me to come to the squadron.

Once every two years we have a visit from the Aerospatiale

test pilot. At the factory they always try to keep one airframe with more hours on it than any of the aircraft they have manufactured and sold. The test pilot, Coffineau, tells us that some of our airframes are doing more hours in a month than some of their clients manage in a year. He checks modifications the Rhodesian Air Force has introduced and goes through our operational techniques. I have been delegated to fly with him. For legal reasons I am the captain of the aircraft – oh yeah, nice one – that means I'm responsible for everything – at this stage it doesn't mean too much, but as the flight progresses I realise why nobody is particularly keen to do this although they are keen on seeing his display routine, which it turns out is the real reason for the flight.

We get airborne and he asks me to take him into the Seke training area, simulating a fireforce-type approach and pull up into the firing orbit. The aircraft is configured in the training role with dual controls fitted and him sitting in the centre seat. We run through some practice engine failures and low-level autorotations and, in response to my question about the limiting speeds for sideways and rearward flight, he demonstrates that they can be safely exceeded by about double the value, but it is extremely uncomfortable as you are being forced out of the seat. On rejoining the airfield I ask for clearance for solo manoeuvring south of the main Salisbury runway. He asks me to demonstrate some torque turns and wingovers and then talks me through a different technique. In conversation about the feasibility of looping an Alouette, he says the main reason is not having enough control authority to get the aircraft up the first part of the loop, and then asks for control. He climbs up and positions back towards the airfield – at this stage I realise that just about the whole station are out on the hard standing around 5 and 7 Squadron hangars and the air force control tower. We dive parallel to the secondary runway and he pulls up hard. It is not quite a loop, but certainly a very, very tight barrel roll, and as we are going over the top he is telling me that I must make sure to have positive 'g' and some collective 'up' at this point to ensure that the blades are coning away from the fuselage.

"And there you see – that is what you can do. Now you have control – you do it."

He talks me through three or four of them and then retakes control and puts a mini display on.

In the middle of this we are just about upside down when Salisbury tower ask us to ensure we are clear of the main runway as the Air Rhodesia viscount is landing. I try to get Coffineau to ease a little southward, but when he does this in Toulouse he must have the airspace to himself, as it doesn't seem to have any effect, but John Hood, the viscount captain comes up on the air and says he has the helicopter visual and is quite OK with it. I look up through the Perspex and see the airliner pass below us. During the next manoeuvre, we have moved away from the runway and he tells me to pull the fuel control shut-off valve and he will demonstrate an engine off landing. I suggest we get right side up but he says to do it straight away – "an engine can fail at any time". As things start going quiet, he gets into a perfectly executed autorotation and as he is cushioning the run on landing, gets his hand on the fuel control lever and restarts the engine as we are doing some three sixty pirouettes on the nosewheel, gets airborne again, chops the engine again and hops over the security fence and uses the momentum of the aircraft to roll into a parking space on the hard standing.

Well, not much to say after that!

We all move to the bar where there has been a party organised in his honour. He is a great raconteur of helicopter tales and advice. His best piece is when he is asked his suggestion for doing a low-level engine-off over rocks or the like, which is very pertinent as this is where we are likely to be shot down in present operations.

"You must flare the aircraft and hold it with nose as high as possible, but do not let the aircraft climb. As the speed decreases, progressively bring the nose more and more to the vertical, so that as the forward speed comes to zero, you have the nose perpendicular to the ground. The aircraft will sink backwards into the ground. The main rotors will hit the ground and break off – and this will absorb much of the energy. Then the tail rotor goes, then the tail boom will crumple. The main fuselage will crumple – and this absorbs much energy. Then whatever is in the cabin will crumple, and this absorbs energy. And then as the aircraft becomes a heap of crumpled wreckage, and all the energy has been taken up, sitting on top of this heap is you – ze pilot – so you can undo your harness and be careful as you climb down."

CHAPTER THIRTEEN

Mapai

The Selous Scouts have taken a heavily armoured column into Mocambique again, led by big John Murphy, an ex US Marine officer who had served in Vietnam. He has transferred to the Scouts, never having recovered into Barney Robinson's good books after spending the battle of Mavue swinging in his parachute harness from a baobab tree.

The column, having bypassed Malvernia, has moved fast down the line of rail and quickly taken out all the enemy positions along it, destroying huge quantities of stores, arms and equipment as far down as Jorge de Limpopo. Here they discover from interrogation of some prisoners that ZANLA has withdrawn its main base to Mapai, further away from the border, so that it is less vulnerable to either air or ground attack.

General Walls gives John the go-ahead to exploit their successes, and leaving behind a rearguard the column move on to take Mapai after a very fierce battle. Having cleared the town of all enemy resistance, the Scouts set about destroying all the installations and arms dumps. They are starting to run low on ammunition and explosives and as the Mapai airfield is secured by our own troops it is decided to send in the Dakota from the Chiredzi fireforce with resupplies and an extra demolition team. It is to return with captured documents, weaponry and the like.

The all ranks' mess at Chiredzi had been built for the security forces by the local farmers, who have massive sugar cane and fruit estates in this region. These farmers are extremely hospitable and there are regular braais and parties. On the inaugural night of the pub's opening, I am there with both Henry Jarvie and Phil Tubbs, and of course Doris. Henry and Phil are performing a number of their routines, and have reached the one where Henry has got most of his kit off and is adopting a classic Greek superhero pose. He has one of the scrawniest bodies you can imagine, and it is difficult to comprehend that he was a champion boxer of some note. Ginger Morris, who in earlier years boxed against him, tells me that when Henry started hitting you, it was so hard and so often you thought you were surrounded. He has acquired a string of sausages and the pose is arranged so that his sports kit is out of sight of the audience, but the sausages have been positioned so that the end is just visible an inch or so above the knee. In the dim light it looks as though there has been an inadvertent slip in the arranging of his anatomy, and there is a lot of covert interest from the wives and daughters, as it seems he is hung like a donkey. Everybody is pretending not to notice, of course, but this is given the lie when Doris comes trotting by, gets a sniff of the meat and turns back and wolfs them in one gulp, causing a collective gasp from the crowd.

We are well into another braai on this night, when news comes through that the Dakota has been shot down whilst taking off from Mapai. It is followed up with the information that there are survivors, but the 'co-pilot' has definitely been killed. This doesn't tell us who is dead as the two pilots, who are both highly experienced captains, switch seats regularly.

ComOps have refused the Scouts' request for helicopter support – they are not going to risk further aircraft.

I call the fireforce to the briefing room and tell them to load full fuel and be ready to get airborne in ten minutes. The ops officer, who is a VR flying officer, asks if he should clear this with ComOps and I tell him that we are positioning forward to Malapati on our side of the border and that he can tell them after we are airborne that he has been having trouble contacting them on the secraphone and we will be listening out on channel two for further instructions. That way if they decide to send us in the morning we will be that much closer. I brief the pilots that we will be lifting from Malapati during the night to arrive at Mapai at first shooting light, which is about fifteen minutes after dawn. The ops officer is not happy about this, but I tell him we are not leaving downed aircrew on the ground over the border and the sooner we act, the easier it will be. Roger Thomas asks if I am asking for volunteers and I tell them all that no, I am not asking for volunteers, I am ordering them to get airborne and I'll take them to where they are going, all they have to do is follow – if there is any fallout to come, they are all following orders.

We arrive at Mapai as a blood red sun is rising over the horizon, and I bring the formation up into an orbit over the airfield. There have been several skirmishes during the night but all is quiet now and there is no firing directed at us. The Scouts say that it is secure for the helicopters to land. I cover the landings of the respective G-Cars whilst they load the crash survivors and the odd casualty from the armoured column and then tell them to cover my own landing.

I touch down close to the command post and see Jerry Lynch, with a blackened face, blood-spattered shirt and looking about seventy years old, escorted out of a shell hole and over to the aircraft. As he is boarding I am being asked over the radio about the body of the other pilot. I'd assumed it would have been loaded on one of the other aircraft, but we are now getting tight on fuel and can't afford to hang about getting a G-Car back on the ground so I tell them to bring it out and load it in the K-Car. I am more than a little shocked to see a package brought out wrapped in black polythene. It bears no resemblance to a body shape at all, and it is placed on the deck between the gun and Jerry, who is sitting in the army commander's seat. As we depart we fly over the still-smouldering skeleton of the Dak.

The Dakota had been called to do a last run late the night before. During the take-off run, a small enemy team had positioned themselves about halfway along the runway. As the aircraft lifted off it was raked with small arms fire and a couple of RPGs launched – one of which at least hit the starboard engine and set it on fire. Jerry tells me that the initial burst of machine gun fire came into the cockpit – there was green tracer flying around – and Bruce was hit in the head and fell over the throttle quadrant. The blood on his shirt is from Bruce's head as he struggled to control and safely force-land the aircraft – he has done a magnificent job, the only serious casualty being Bruce. The six other passengers have survived with minor bruising, scratches and a few scorches. The cargo was half a dozen bloody heavy plant tyres that were being taken back to Rhodesia!

We arrive back at Malapati shortly after a light fixed-wing has touched down. There is a welcoming committee of minor brass from Salisbury, which turns out to be the Board of Inquiry into the incident. Jerry has got out and wandered over to them whilst I am getting the aircraft shut down. I debus and as I get up to this little group I hear them asking him if he was sure Bruce Collocott was dead before he abandoned the aircraft. I grab Criv and tell him to take Jerry away for breakfast and then tear into these guys. He has been shot down, his friend's blood is all over him, he's done a magnificent job in producing a survivable crash landing, spends the night in Indian country being shot at, and before he has even had time for a cup of tea he is being interrogated. They back off.

ComOps now decide that it is a good idea to have the helicopters positioned close to the border and we are tasked with taking in a salvage team to dismantle anything recoverable from the wreck and a demolition team and explosives to destroy the remains.

★

Willie Knight and I are leaning at the Chiredzi bar, a few beers consumed, when the barman closes the bar. We ask for more, but are told it is the camp commandant's new policy that the bar closes promptly at eleven. We argue with him that that is fine as far as the other ranks are concerned, but as officers we have been flying all day, and to leave the fridge open and we'll settle the account in the morning. He is adamant, however, and having padlocked the fridge disappears.

Big Willie hops over the counter and bends the restraining bar enough that we can replenish, so we carry on, making an accurate note of what we are consuming.

Some fifth columnist informs the barman, who in turn wakes the camp commandant, Tommy R, a VR on call-up duties. He arrives with the duty guard detachment who all look about twelve years old; they are a new batch of national serviceman. He orders them to escort us off the premises.

Like Willie, I am severely embarrassed by the subsequent disgraceful events, even after a couple of decades have passed, so will offer my only pathetic excuse in advance – you cannot be ordered to bed by a man wearing shortie silk pyjamas. We are out jousting day after day after day, and I am being told to go to bed by a man in short silk pyjamas. No.

Neither of us can remember how the first bottle leaves the bar, arcs into the revolving fan and airbursts into a thousand fragments, but it stops the teenagers in their tracks. As they are urged forward by Tommy we continue to exploit our new-found airburst weapon fully. Intriguingly, nobody thinks of turning the fan off, but Tommy encourages his troops by pointing out that we can't keep this up much longer as the supply of empties is nearly diminished.

Silly. Silly. The fridge is open, and there is a near limitless supply of full bottles, which are in fact a far more effective deterrent, as on bursting there is also a spray of beer. He and his hit team leave. We reconcile the extra full bottles we now owe for with our bar account, the empties were already on apart from the deposit value of the bottles themselves, and settle back into putting the wrongs of the world right.

After about twenty minutes our nemesis has returned, and this time with a different escort – he has organised the guard detachment from Support Commando. These are the extremely tough soldiers of the RLI that we carry into combat every day. They seem to be a little bewildered but do look pretty tough – they are! He orders them to take us under armed guard to the army guardroom. The corporal of the guard looks at him questioningly.

Willie has his pistol out – things have just taken a giant leap.

"The first man that moves, I'll fucking shoot!"

Wow, that's got everybody's attention.

The RLI corporal, a former British army para, is the only person throughout the saga who shows any sort of common sense. The commandant has made a bad judgement; we work with these people on the edge of life almost every day.

"Sir. I don't know what's going on here, but these gentlemen

kill people for a living. Mister Borlace there is like Doc
Holliday with a sawn-off K-Car up his sleeve. And I have to
walk underneath it every day."

Come on, it is Willie who is doing the gunslinger routine.

"These two pilots keep us alive. This is officer shite. You
sort it out your fooking self."

On that note, he gets his men outside and they march away.

Tommy disappears, and at some stage Willie and I
obviously get turned in, because in the morning Sod's Law is
in gear and the callout siren is wailing at first light. There is an
absolute confirmed sighting of a large group to our north-west.

Tommy is in the army ops room; at least he has got a
dressing gown over the shorties.

"You two are grounded, we're just sending the two G-Cars."
The other two very junior pilots are looking very pasty faced
and the army commander is just about to protest.

"Piss off, Tommy, they're not going anywhere without us."
He has no authority whatsoever to even be involved with ops.

"Group Captain Pink is already on his way down in a
Canberra from Salisbury to deal with you both."

"No prob. We'll see him when we get back."

Nigel Henson, Support Commando OC, looks mightily
relieved as we ignore any further interruption and get the
brief out of the way. Henson and I have had a spectacular
bust-up in a previous deployment. There have been a couple
of modifications made to K-Cars at my suggestion, and he
has heard that the 'mute' switch for muting out garrulous
army commanders who are blocking out radio exchanges is
one of them. Funnily enough, I never actually use the device
myself, but the argument is monumental about its possible
employment – to the point where both the army and air force
send senior officers to interview us separately with a view to
separating us from a joint deployment. They are surprised

that, quite independently, we make it plain that we are more than happy to work with each other, we just don't want to mix socially. By this stage, we have a reasonable rapport and he is quietly pulling my leg as we pass the 'Canberra of Retribution', which is on finals as we depart for today's match.

It is a good day, but it does take all day to sort out. There is the occasional request from Chiredzi that if possible Spider Zero Seven and Spider One Two are to recover as soon as possible as long as it doesn't affect operational capability, but it is half-hearted; they know it is me who will make the decisions, and nobody is surprised when it is the two of us who fly back last after last light like two naughty schoolboys trying to avoid the headmaster.

During this punch-up, I have directed Willie onto an LZ to drop some troops close to where we estimate the gooks are. He confirms he has the LZ visual, and I change to reading one of the other helicopters onto a different LZ. There is a sudden screeching on the radio. As Willie flares to land, the gooks stand up and give him a snottie; he pulls collective and aborts the landing fast.

Now he comes back on the radio – the soldiers in the back have told him the stick leader has already jumped out, he is on his own in the same LZ as the gooks. We get on top with the gunship double quick and slam down a lot of prophylactic fire as all three G-Cars offload their troops close by. The soldiers get into the LZ and call us – they have found the stick leader alive with a smoking FN and a lot of dead gooks. He is Russell Phillips, a corporal who has just two weeks ago been awarded a Silver Cross for extricating an officer from a cave – sadly, Jerry Fisher died – where he ends up just using his pistol and his mates are throwing in loaded magazines to keep him resupplied with ammunition. When we speak to him subsequently about this present escapade he just says "What else was I going to do? Resign?" He is put up for an immediate bar to the SCR, but the Rhodesians naturally wrap the two episodes together into one citation.

★

We arrive back and it transpires that Chris Dixon, the new Canberra squadron commander, is not yet night, qualified so they have had to stay for the night.

Willie and I have separate one-sided, and very definitely without coffee, interviews with Len Pink, who is the new station commander at Sarum. He deals with it pretty well, and fairly. We will pay for the damage – there isn't actually a lot – and he is impressed that we did keep a running account of what was either being drunk or exploded. Willie and I will not be deployed on operations together again; we'll do four duties as night duty officer at New Sarum during our next four R and Rs, and we are banned from all air force bars for a week. The pistol incident is not brought up. Then my opinion of navigators goes up – not a lot, but a little – when he announces that the punishment will only commence tomorrow and joins us in the bar to celebrate today's outing. Then it goes up again when he buys the first round – what is happening? This is unheard of for a navigator.

The terms of contrition are impossible to fulfil; the squadron can hardly keep to its commitments without introducing a 'he can only fly with him and not with him' policy as well, and Willie and I are at Mtoko together within a month. Because we are at Sarum so rarely and randomly, it is just easier for the adjutant to forget the 'duty officer' bit – I think we both actually do just one; and Peter Hengiston, one of the VR ops officers at Chiredzi, who is a 'baron' on one of the local sugar estates, takes all the off-duty aircrew down to his home every night, which becomes 'Number Two Mess' until my ban is expired. He has a lovely wife, and a delightful daughter of about thirteen, who a couple of years later goes with the Zimbabwe Ladies' hockey team at their first Olympics.

Always some of the other farming families turn up, we have some great parties, nobody tells us to go to bed – there might be the odd whispered request from one of the daughters, who don't get to meet too much new meat in the area, and we are always ready for work before first light.

CHAPTER FOURTEEN

Dingo

We are ordered to bring the fireforce back to New Sarum from Mtoko. On arrival there are many helicopters parked on the 7 Squadron hardstanding. We are told to remove all of our personal kit from the machines and the aircraft are to be lubed and all minor snags rectified whilst the pilots are briefed by Ted Lunt to prepare for an extended high-density operation that will be briefed when the rest of the aircraft arrive. He will not be drawn on further questioning, but adds that we are all confined to the airfield and no telephone calls are to be made off station.

Throughout the afternoon more helicopters arrive until it is apparent every machine on the squadron is there, with all the current aircrew along with a whole lot of former members, both pilots and gunners who have been drafted in for their call-ups or attached from other duties – there isn't enough room for us all in the hangar and offices.

Eventually the pilots are briefed. Operation Dingo is to be a massive airstrike on ZANLA's main base in Mocambique, New Farm at Chimoi, which is a complex of 17 camps covering about 25 square kilometres. The airstrike is to be followed by an airborne landing of paratroops and heliborne soldiers covered by K-Cars. The camps are located over 90 kilometres from the eastern border. The initial airstrike will use all the air forces' offensive capability – Hunters, Canberras and Vampires laying down various combinations of Golf, Alpha and HE bombs, cannon and rocket strikes and frantans – followed up by K-Cars and Lynx aircraft on target as the Paradaks and G-Cars are dropping their troops.

The plan is stunning in its audacity and innovation. Although heavily defended by anti-aircraft weaponry, the enemy, estimated as between five and ten thousand, will not expect to be engaged by heliborne forces as they know our helicopters do not have the range to reach their base from our borders with troops. The solution to this problem is to designate ten helicopters, carrying self-protection troops, defensive mortars and reserve ammunition, to land and hold an LZ/DZ area north of the target where the DZ will be immediately marked for the DC-7 attached to 3 Squadron to airdrop 80 drums of fuel. The helicopters on target will then transit to this 'administrative area' to rearm and refuel as required from the target. Thus, we will be able to maintain continuous air cover with gunship support for the troops on the target and fly casualties quickly to be medically stabilised before onward airlift to hospitals in Rhodesia.

H-hour for the start of the strikes is 07:45. The troop landings are to commence at 07:50, with the paratroops dropped in two lines along the south-eastern and south-western edges of a containment box designed to try and keep the fleeing enemy in the killing zone, with the north-western edge troops dropped by G-Cars and the ten gunships completing the box with a free-fire zone to hopefully drive the enemy back into the area they have fled from. The total number of our soldiers being inserted into the fight is 184 – the whole of the SAS and two commandos from the RLI.

My designation is K-10. As the helicopters run in, the gunships have all been allocated individual targets to engage and neutralise as we cross over the camp to close the lid on the killing zone. We have been allocated a target designated as

'New Garage' complex on the gridded air photos we have been issued with in lieu of maps, and it is the furthest east of them, which means we will have a long approach over the main camp area. Crivellari is to be my gunner and we take our individual briefing documents away and study them, at one point going to the photo-interpretation section to discuss our target. We are unhappy about some features that look like gun pits around the complex, but the photo people, although they can't positively say what they are, consider they are probably areas used by witch doctors for ceremonies. Hmm.

The battle is to be controlled by Norman Walsh and Brian Robinson, in a specially modified K-Car that has extra radios so that they can communicate with individual stop groups and aircraft as well as General Walls and his team who will be in a Warthog command Dakota, itself able to have direct comms with ComOps and the Prime Minister's office in case some strategic decisions have to be made in the event of attempted FPLM intervention or a major loss, for example. Every individual has a copy of the same gridded air photo in order to preclude snafus with locations of targets or friendly troops.

All the participants are strictly quarantined until we commence our operation, being woken at 03:00 on Wednesday 23rd November.

Thirty-one helicopters are lined up with crews in the pre-dawn whilst Air Marshal Frank Mussell comes along and gives everybody a personal rah-rah chat. Part of the well-wishing is that he regrets not being able to participate himself. Baldie offers to let him have his place, but he moves along to the next crew. We start a phased departure of five-ship formations at 04:30 and our first destination is Lake Alexander. Here we refuel and the G-Cars embark their pre-designated loads.

Harold Griffiths is to lead the strike and assault force of twenty-one helicopters, with the other ten lifting about fifteen minutes later. As we approach the high ground inside Mocambique, cloud is blocking the valley we have planned to pass through, so Harold takes the formation back out and searches for another passage. We are starting to get late for our ToT, but the order comes to stay with the plan and we must get through as soon as we can.

The first evolution in the strike is at four minutes before H-hour. Affretair's DC-8 flies directly over the camp on a north-easterly heading, flaps down making as much noise as possible, simulating a commercial flight outbound from Maputo up to Malawi. This is to deliberately warn the enemy air watch guards and allow them to take cover until they see it is a commercial jet, when they will relax and return into normal camp routine.

At 07:45, the war gets noisy as three Hunters initiate the strike throwing two frantans and four golf bombs onto the muster parades and targets in the main complex as four FB9 Vampires strike the recruits' camp with strafing 20mm attacks and 60lb rocket salvoes. Thirty seconds later, a pair of Canberras unload 600 alpha bombs across the headquarters whilst another pair unload their full loads on the other side of the camp. At H-hour plus two minutes, the two paradropping formations of three Dakotas, each flying at right angles to each other, start their dropping runs using a slow exit rate in order to ensure a good separation of troops arriving on the ground. They are escorted by four Hunters and a pair of Vampires who are striking known anti-aircraft emplacements with 68mm rockets and 30mm cannon and 60lb rockets and 20mm cannon as appropriate.

We appear out of the murk as this is going on; we are about five minutes behind time, but that doesn't seem to have been too much of a problem. There is smoke and dust all over the camps with streams of red and green tracer and we see jets putting in restrikes and secondary explosions throughout the complex.

As we start to cross over the main camp area – we are at sixteen hundred feet – Delta Zero, Norman Walsh, the battle commander, transmits that they have taken a heavy hit and are pulling off to the admin area, handing over airborne control to Griffiths, and Robinson orders the ground troops to hold their ground locations and reorganise until he returns in a replacement helicopter. The other K-Cars, including us, are free to react independently to any fire support requests from callsigns on the ground – which works perfectly well as we are all well-versed in this from fireforce work – as well as engaging targets of opportunity and completing our initial target tasks. As our own troops are temporarily static there is little danger of a friendly fire snafu from the gunships, and there are none, but during some of the fixed-wing strikes that are called in there are a couple of very nasty incidents. Thankfully there are no deaths caused by the jet pilots attacking our own troops.

'Targets of opportunity' are a-plenty and we have used about half our ammunition before we get above New Garage. Although we personally don't seem to be taking any large-calibre fire, the small arms flak and some 12.7 is unbelievable. There is a continuous buzzing sound of small-calibre automatic fire punctuated by cracks of the stuff that is close and thumps as we take regular hits, and this goes on throughout the day.

We arrive over the garage complex and Criv gives it a good working over and then we spend some time jousting with the weapons that have been sited in the 'witch doctor's ceremonial pits'. Hmm.

Eventually the airborne commanders get back in another G-Car that has been rapidly reconfigured into a substitute command aircraft and the sweeps are continued. A cab rank system of K-Cars is instituted with two or three aircraft orbiting the camp complex and called in to provide support for any callsign as required – the other gunships being rearmed and refuelled at the admin area and on instant readiness for recall to the battle. The technicians are undertaking battle damage repairs continuously and keep the helicopters serviceable. The small arms flak is very heavy and doesn't let up throughout the day. We are all flying higher than normally for gunship duties and the flak comes over as a continuous buzzing sound, punctuated by cracking of the closer stuff and the regular hits. I think every helicopter over the target had taken multiple strikes within the first five minutes of the attack.

However, you do sort of get used to it – amazing as that sounds. Suddenly though there is a squawking over the radio from one of the K-Cars – it is Mark McLean.

"Come on, Mugsy, we're all big boys. You've got to take your share," from Baldie.

"Yes, but I've just been shot in the fucking head."

That shuts up all the chatter on the radio. I leave the cabrank shortly after and return to the admin area for fuel and ammunition and whilst there see Mark, who has just been initially treated and is about to be casevaced back to Umtali. It is a real 'John Wayne movie' wound. A round has hit his eyebrow and it hasn't even split the skin, although there is a fearsome bruise and swelling, and he is quite compos mentis. You start to wonder about the complex factors involved – half a knot slower, or faster, a foot more or less of altitude, a fraction of a second difference of whoever pulled the trigger – but decide very quickly not to ponder too long and thank the Lord he's been so lucky. I'd been in a fireforce some while back when Doug Sinclair had taken a round in the head. Their aircraft went straight to Fort Victoria hospital, and Doug was agitated about them removing his helmet as he could feel warm liquid dripping down his neck and he thought his head might fall to pieces if it came off. It transpired that the warm liquid was the gel filling of his intercom ear pad which had been punctured by a round passing between his head and the inside of his helmet hitting the earphone, and causing Bakelite shrapnel around his ear only.

★

We are recalled to the cabrank, but the ground battle seems to have been largely won and we are not asked for any ground support for a while, although there is still plenty of flak causing the continuous buzz in the air. I ask Criv to pass me a water bottle from the back, but there is no reply. I ask again and there is no response.

I loosen my straps and ease myself forward so that I can look back around my armoured seat. He is slumped in his seat.

"Christ. The little bastard has been hit."

I ease out of the flak area, loosen my straps right off and reach around to see if I can do anything as we head for the admin area where the medical triage area has been established. As I shake him, he comes to life – unbelievably, he has fallen asleep. I am so relieved, and he is so embarrassed, that not too much is said other than the regular joshing afterwards, but he tries to avoid seeing me as the years pass, as he knows it is going to cost him a beer every time.

Geoff Dartnall's techs have done a magnificent job throughout the day keeping the helos serviceable, with two complete changes of main rotor blades, one tail rotor change, one complete engine change plus all the battle damage in a grass vlei we have commandeered in Mocambique. Plus, all of them have been doing their flying duties as required, and will be lubing and daily servicing their aircraft on return to Umtali.

As the G-Cars start lifting out intelligence materials, some prisoners, captured heavy weaponry and some of the troops, they are escorted out in small formations by a K-Car to the Lake Alexander assembly point and eventually, as night comes in, to Grand Reef Umtali.

It has been a very long day – when I finally shut down I have flown eleven hours twenty, half an hour of it at night, and have probably been in the cockpit for another three hours on top of that, with a lot of the airborne time spent being ferociously shot at.

The caterers, led by John Crewell, have produced a magnificent meal, but somewhat surprisingly the beer drinking doesn't go on too long as everybody is shattered. We learn that the initial assessment is that the exercise has been a resounding success and that we have lost one soldier killed and a handful wounded and one Vampire lost. Phil Haigh lost his engine over the target and was gliding to a forced landing in Rhodesia, during which he was killed. The FB9s don't have bang seats, which rather limits your options when you've lost the engine.

The next morning, we continue to escort the G-Cars in and out during their clear up and extraction flights. I don't recall that a single shot was fired at the helicopters all day, and the battlefield, blackened, smoking and covered in bodies, looks like a scene from the Great War. Some of the ambush troops left overnight have had punch-ups during the night, but any terrorist survivors are keeping very quiet and out of sight now. The last callsign on the ground is Bob MacKenzie with a troop of SAS who has commandeered a Peugeot pick-up. I cover the troopers' uplift and touch down briefly to lift Bob off as the very last man, just for the hell of it really.

We are just getting stuck into a bacon and egg breakfast when Griff gives us the good news.

★

This exercise was Zulu One; we have actually only got to half-time and we are to immediately reposition for another strike, Zulu Two, on another camp complex. Chimoi was about eighty-odd kilometres over the eastern border. Tembue is two hundred and twenty kilometres over the northern border. We are going to launch initially from Mtoko, and refuel three times, at Darwin, Chiswiti and on the 'train', an isolated mountain in Mocambique, before crossing the Caborra Bassa lake and striking the camp with the helicopters on very low fuel, then pulling off to our refuelling and rearming base situated five minutes to the west. I am tasked with taking a battle-damaged aircraft to Salisbury and positioning at Darwin after repairs, hopefully in time to join in the initial wave as they pass through in the morning.

The aircraft is not ready before last light, and the weather looks too bad for a night flight out to FAF 4, so I get in a bit of recreational playtime for the evening and get airborne before dawn the next morning to arrive there in time to fill in with the assault force.

The camp complex is more sprawling than Chimoi and a lot of the inhabitants are located in the thick forest line along the river that the photo interpreters haven't seen. Apparently, we also just miss a large number who are moved out of the camp the day before we strike. However, the jet strikes go in on target and cause a lot of damage before we get there as the paratroops are landing. There is intense groundfire, but it seems to be mostly small arms, and although we are taking hits, it doesn't seem to be as accurate as Chimoi – maybe we are just getting used to it. With the admin base being just five minutes away, we get a much faster turnaround time. The ground battle is, for all intents and purposes, over by lunch time and the G-Cars start their extrications, moving in groups of six escorted by a gunship. Bob MacKenzie calls me for his callsign to be uplifted from a narrow and long LZ. We land in line ahead so the sticks can load easily. I am in the lead aircraft and I tell Bob he is getting slack as he has left one of the gooks alive. Right in front of me one of the bodies rolls over and time slows right down as it is obvious he is not wounded at all and has been playing dead. He deliberately aims his AK straight at me from about ten feet away. I have always had a contingency plan for this scenario, which is to throw the helicopter directly at the terrorist, but there is a stump between the nose and this guy. I screech for immediate uplift of all the aircraft and start pulling collective as I see his muzzle flaming and hear gunshots going off as I lift over him. There is massive fire from the callsign on the ground and my own gunner lets rip, although afterwards he admits he hadn't seen anything, but as everyone else was firing it seemed like a good idea. One of the fixed-wings afterwards said the six helicopters erupted out of the bush like corks. From ten feet away the guy misses the cockpit completely and his rounds all go high, striking the rotors. Go figure!

Having got ourselves reorganised, stopped hyperventilating, and been persuaded that all the bodies in the LZ are now dysfunctional, we are persuaded by Bob to come back in and pull them out.

★

Shortly afterwards, I am tasked with getting down to the area of grids to the south of the target where trooping aircraft proceeding en route back to Rhodesia are being harassed by small arms fire in the vicinity of what appears to be a road building camp. We get down there and circling over a group of graders and bulldozers sure enough get a fairly substantial snottie. We quickly roll port and get a group of terrorists visual who are firing at us and immediately engage them – several drop on the spot and the others hightail into the bush with the exception of one who decides to run along the road, giving us the odd squirt until presumably his magazine becomes empty. We can't get a sighting picture for a short while, but he stays in the road so we reposition and send a long burst down which really spoils his day for him. We move back to the road equipment but attract no more fire so I get the gunner to fire a number of bursts into the engine and hydraulic blocks, tyres, etc: there is little point in firing at what are essentially armoured vehicles. Interestingly, I am interviewed several days after this. It is not actually the classic 'one-sided without tea and biscuits' meeting, but initially I am told that I mustn't let 'blood-lust' curb my judgement. I am astounded, and make my normal comment that if people fire at me or those I am responsible for, they are going to get a snottie back double quick and that within the last few days, we had alpha and golf bombed literally thousands of our enemies before using tens of thousands of cannon ammunition on the survivors of the initial attacks. It transpires that the vehicles we have destroyed belong to a South African company who are building the road. I just say that I am not going to comment on why one of our allies is building infrastructure that is assisting our enemy to more easily move his soldiers around.

It is decided to send the majority of helicopters back to Rhodesia in a sort of formation of formations, with groups of five or six assembling together and then joining up in about twenty-odd at the assembly area prior to setting sail for Chiswiti and points over

SPIDER ZERO SEVEN   195

our border. The fuel and the weight of either personnel or cargo has been calculated by the planning staff and handed to aircraft commanders. I do a mental appraisal of space/time/distance and tell my technician for the trip to add on at least another hundred and fifty and, if he can squeeze it out of any drums, preferably two hundred pounds. I and a couple of experienced fireforce commanders point out to one of the staff people overseeing this preparation and despatch of the flying circus that these figures are not going to work and leave us no contingency. Basically, we are told that the figures have been carefully calculated to get us to the 'train' in the most efficient manner.

The first thing that hasn't been taken into account is how long it takes twenty-odd aircraft to get airborne and orbit as we have been ordered to do before setting heading. The day is starting to drift along too and we have actually orbited four times when a couple of the mini-formation elements, me included, announce we are starting to go as the final aircraft are still fannying about getting into the air. I check my fuel gauge and remark that there are going to be people that aren't going to have enough fuel onboard already. About ten minutes later, Terrance Murphy announces that he is returning for more fuel as he is not going to proceed without more. He is a highly experienced operator, very used to working down to low fuel states, and having been questioned over the radio about what he is doing, basically tells whoever is querying his judgement to get off the air and get some drums ready for immediate use. He and about four helicopters return to the admin area – showing excellent airmanship, as far as I am concerned.

We get to top-up on the 'train' and are departing as the crowd are starting to arrive, with a number bleating about wanting priority arrival as they are on serious red light. I manage to get my little herd on its way as chaos is starting. One helicopter has landed on an island in the middle of Lake Caborra Bassa and they are trying to arrange an airdrop of fuel drums to it.

Having lifted from the 'train' it looks like some mean storm lines are developing to the south.

I had insisted that the helicopters I was shepherding were all fat on fuel and, along with two other formations, we decide to bypass Chiswiti and proceed directly towards the Zambezi escarpment whilst the weather is still navigable. However, the storm comes in very quickly. Bill Sykes is leading a little gaggle just off to our left and announces that he is going to try and make Darwin; I can hear people to the rear of us announcing that they are going to go for Chiswiti and stay there and a couple say they are going for Darwin. I can see a long grey tunnel that offers a clearish path generally in the direction of Centenary and lead us that way. It gets darker and darker and I recognise one of the farms to the north of the Centenary and lead us in to land close to the main farmhouse.

We are royally fed and watered – or more truthfully 'beer and wined' – and bedded down for the night comfortably by the family, who are all aware that something big has been going on but accept the details are not going to be promulgated straight away.

The next morning, the weather having cleared, we are able to get airborne and hop over to Darwin. Bill Sykes is already there – he'd told his various followers to break off and look after themselves and managed to find his way into Darwin, whereupon, after landing, he is astonished to find another aircraft that lands right alongside him who had decided to look after himself by closing up into close formation and doggedly staying there until his leader took him to a safe arrival.

It takes until lunch time before all the helicopters scattered over the countryside are located and fuel has gone to those where none was available locally, although most of them have landed in secure places, before we reassemble and confirm that there have been no losses either due to enemy action or the bad weather.

★

A major complication is that three of the pilots are under close arrest. Baldie, Delport and Willie Knight have had a loud verbal disagreement with Barney Barnes, the station warrant officer from Sarum who has 'ordered' them to stop drinking and go to bed. Unfortunately, Barney has a massive and fatal heart attack not long afterwards, and their hindships are considering charging the pilots with causing his death. Of course, ultimately that eventually doesn't go anywhere, mostly because Prof Christie, one of the reserve Dakota pilots involved in the raids, is also the Dean of Law at the university and straightens everybody out with the legalities. On a selfish note, I am hacked off as Barney owes me a crate of beer, won in a head-to-head three round down-down race of pints of beer from a couple of nights before.

Back to New Sarum, twenty-four hours off whilst the aircraft are serviced and then I take a five-aircraft fireforce down to Gwanda, which is the JOC for a new operational area, Op Tangent.

A slight drifting off course after refuelling at Thornhill allows me to call in with them for afternoon tea at a girlfriend's ranch on the way.

CHAPTER FIFTEEN

Chiqualaquala

It is coming up to Christmas and I am leading a two-aircraft detachment supporting SAS operations deep into Mocambique to the east of the railway line.

The other crew changeover takes place two days before Christmas. We have just been requested to go in and haul out one of the callsigns who have been compromised and are on the run, when their replacement crew arrives. I tell them to handover to the new crew quickly and then send the pilot along for briefing as they will otherwise miss this Dakota, which is operated on a round-the-houses schedule and will not be able to wait for them.

The new guy arrives, and he is new. It is the first time I have met him as he is straight out of training, where he won the sword of honour, and this is his first day on bush operations. I apologise that he is being thrown straight into ops and start to go through the plan. He is looking like a stunned mullet. It crosses my mind that it hasn't cropped up in training that penetrating deep into Mocambique, not aerobatics or instrument flying practice, is the everyday work on the squadron in this part of the world. He gets into query mode and wants to know why we are going as Red formation, when they've been taught the allocated colours for helicopter formations are Yellow, Pink and Amber – because if there are any enemy listening posts monitoring our RT they may just think we are a couple of jets coming down and be looking for the wrong aircraft in the wrong places – why are we are using these frequencies, why we are putting this amount of fuel in and not this amount, why are we going down using a series of different headings, not in a straight line – because they are to places I know and can recognise in the almost featureless flatlands. This is all good stuff in flying school but time is moving on and I am rather abrupt in telling him that this is a briefing and not a question and answer session, so listen. I feel guilty to see his crestfallen look, but we finish the brief and launch off to the south-east.

The hot-extraction goes off OK, but he has to go in and do the actual uplift whilst I put down covering fire and he collects a severe snottie from the Freds on the ground. The poor chap doesn't look quite so bright-eyed and bushy-tailed that evening. Twenty-four hours ago he was having his last night in Salisbury, the junior ace of the base, and now he's teamed up with a grumpy autocrat who leads him miles over Africa and sends him in to meet some even worse-tempered people who are intent on killing him.

Christmas Day starts with everybody getting a parcel from the WVS. Mine contains a balaclava, some mittens with the finger tops missing – the temperature is routinely thirty-five Celsius down here – an orange, a writing pad and a pack of playing cards. The weather is appalling today – wet and with a very low cloud/mist which is called a 'guti'. It is barely flyable, but mid-morning we get a call to pull out an SAS callsign. Alastair, the new guy, is much quieter and more attentive in this briefing.

We set off down the way. The visibility is non-existent but we reach the massive power-lines that run parallel to the border some way inside Mocambique at the right time, alter heading more to the south, and continue down to the pick-up point.

In this part of the world there is a huge magnetic anomaly and our compasses are useless; we set a directional gyro but that drifts off heading and should be realigned every twenty minutes if possible. In this sort of weather it is impossible, due to not being able to see any definite landmarks.

We do the pick-up without any drama and start the long haul back through the guti. We are flying in a loose battle echelon about five hundred yards apart, which is the limit of visibility.

Through the murk in front of me, something looks strange. We are covering five hundred yards about every six seconds. I am still trying to rationalise this strange appearance of the ground when I realise we have come too far to the left and it is the railway line ahead – we are nearly on top of it. There is an eruption of tracer, RPG bursts, at least three Strellas loop into the sky, a cacophony of very heavy automatic fire and the thumping of heavier guns. I scream into the radio, "Break right! Break right!" and drop my collective. It is Chiqualaquala siding, which is very heavily defended, and I have led us right to it. There is a cutting which I drop into turning right, levelling and straightening along the line of rail.

"Open fire!"

Mark Furnell needs no urging and as we hurtle along below the top of the cutting I can hear the gun thumping away behind me. In an amazing frieze of time almost suspended I can see the startled faces of gooks scrambling around on the embankments and diving for cover on the tracks. We are so low that we would hit any man standing and the heavy guns cannot depress to fire at us. I think, ludicrously, as the lines of tracer stand out against the grey overcast providing a tunnel we are flying through, "This is just like the movies."

We are being fired at from both sides of the tracks, and although we are taking multiple hits they must be causing carnage amongst themselves also, as they are firing into each other. It is obvious that this is going to be a one-way trip to a spectacular hole in the ground unless I do something quick. Right or left? I'm not sure if it is a conscious decision but I tell Mark to hold on and rack on a hard turn to the right. We pull three, maybe four, G, and take several more hits as we cross back through the line of fire and then we are away. About thirty seconds have passed since the shooting started.

I am slightly surprised but delighted to see the other helicopter about a mile away in a right-hand orbit. On my "Break right!" he had immediately and unquestioningly broken right into safety – thank god it wasn't Bill 'of a thousand questions' Michie, who would probably have asked "Why?" His last view of us had been the massive upburst of tracer, explosions, Strella trails and us disappearing below the trees and, as far as he knew, into the ground. He is trying to sort out where he is and is both astonished and relieved to hear me call.

I tell him I will fly across his nose, he is to follow me and do a visual check of the aircraft as we have been hit badly and may be streaming fuel or even on fire. He acknowledges as I whistle past his nose but hasn't replied as to our state after half a minute. When I ask him what the story is, he tells me he can't catch us up. The collective is up under my left arm where I'd pulled the gut-wrenching turn out of the fireworks display and we have probably set a new speed record for the Alouette. I let it back to a more normal level and as we stop hyperventilating he flies up alongside, says that he can't see any fluid streams or smoke, and Furnell and the SAS troops in his aircraft exchange funny faces and various obscene and encouraging hand signals.

I know where there is a TA company position just on our side of the border and we head for there to land, refuel and check for damage. Mark and I also need to check our underpants. The TF guys haven't seen any helicopters during their deployment and ask if we are on a border patrol flight as they have had no indication of gooks in the area for weeks. We can hear a massive artillery exchange going on just to our west, and they tell us that Malvernia started stonking Vila Salazar about ten minutes beforehand and they wonder what set that off. None of us say anything. It is a different war for them.

Our aircraft has been hit forty-seven times, but amazingly absolutely nothing vital has been hit, although both Mark and I have holes very close to our swedes, and the helicopter just needs a lot of patching in the next few days.

We transit back to Hooters and I sit and eat my orange quietly, before getting stuck into our Christmas feast and then all of us getting thoroughly plastered. Alastair joins in enthusiastically; he has flown on two ops, been shot at and hit on his first and seen this debacle on his second. He has also survived and things cannot get much worse, can they?

After I send the airstrike report I receive a signal which asks if I would like to comment on the cost of artillery and the 20mm ammunition consequences of my navigational error, in tones of barely concealed sarcasm. I reply with a short message:

"John, chapter, 11 verse 35."

The correspondence ceases.

CHAPTER SIXTEEN

Rio

Eventually we are starting to get the benefit of an expansion of the training of pilots, and the rather reluctant acceptance of the staff in allowing some of them straight onto helicopters – previously they have had to spend a tour on one of the other squadrons before coming on to 7 Squadron. A few months ago there had been an experiment with Nic Meikle and Mark Dawson, the youngest pilot to gain his wings in Rhodesia, being sent straight from training for a heli-conversion and deployment, and they have both performed very well.

Nic has survived being shot down. We were experimenting with dropping bomblets containing tear gas to flush the enemy out of thick bush, but were giving our own troops as many problems as we were solving with their use. Nic had the aircraft with the panniers carrying the bomblets and got hit by some small arms fire that also ignited the canisters, causing the crew a lot of grief during their descent and forced landing.

I am on a break from the bush – at the time we were getting about four days off for every six weeks plus on ops – and catching up on sleep in single quarters at Sarum when the telephone starts ringing incessantly. There doesn't appear to be anybody going to answer it, so despite my long-held belief that you should never pick up a phone if you're not actually expecting a call, I throw a towel around my waist and take the call. An imperious female voice demands to know who she is talking to before informing me that she wants to speak with Air

Sub Lieutenant Dawson, who at this stage I have never heard of, who is a helicopter pilot, and to tell him that his mother wants to talk with him. I ask her to hold, check the board with the cabin allocations, and sure enough, sod's law is working well; he not only lives in the cabin that is physically furthest from the phone, he is, of course, not in it when I get there.

On passing this information, however, I am not released from the phone: she has apparently been told my name and I am exhorted to do my best to look after her little boy when he is in the bush. I assure her that we do actually know what we are doing on operations – that's not stretching the truth too much – and Mark will be very closely monitored as to what he does on early sorties. She is still not satisfied, and asks if there is a chance he will be sent to the Eastern Highlands, which of course is almost a certainty. I am then informed that he has always had a susceptibility to sore throats and will I personally make sure he wears a scarf during the cold mornings.

Of course I will, I'll even blow his nose for him and wash behind his ears if it means I can get away from the phone and get back to sleep.

As it happens, Mark spends quite a lot of his early detachments with the fireforce I run, and very quickly becomes a good operator. It is in Umtali, after we've had a good day of slaying gooks and are having a party in the all ranks' bar – it must be a weekend because there are several local girls out from the town; there is normally an armed convoy that does the runs to pick them up and take them back, and quite often an illicit helo trip into the town the following morning to drop off any stragglers – when I see Mark, who is perhaps getting a little full of himself, doing a 'there I was' routine with full use of both hands impressing a couple of young lovelies, that I decide it is time to bring up the scarf story, which I've kept in reserve until now. He's never forgiven me.

Towards the end of the war, the poor bugger has his tail
rotor drive taken out by some heavy flak, and spins into the
ground. Amazingly, both of the crew survive, but Mark has
severe brain damage – his air supply is blocked for some time
before he can be released from the wreckage – and he has never
fully recovered from either that or the pain that accompanies
other injuries he'd received. Another life uselessly blighted.

I have a heavy fireforce consisting of two K-Cars and five
troopers at Buffalo Range, but it is manned totally by a new
intake of pilots. Mark Dawson is in fact the most experienced
of them and therefore mans the second gunship by default. He's
not exactly over enthused about the prospect. Generally, when
they first come on the squadron, everybody wants to get onto
the K-Car, but nowadays there is so much flak hitting them, it's
not so popular. Quite a lot of the pilots neither want to fly that
slot nor have some of the attributes required to operate in that
capacity. Horses for courses.

Our first outing is an external strike against a camp named
Rio, so we position forward to Malapati in the late afternoon
of the day before.

There is a bit of a drama during the transit. By sheer
chance, we fly right over the top of a gook camp in the bush.
A combination of favourable wind direction and our height
has covered the sound of our approach, and I suddenly see
some pots and packs, and then a number of bodies scurrying
for cover. I pull up hard in a climbing left turn and Finch
Bellringer, a very good gunner who is quick on the uptake,
starts laying down accurate fire immediately. I consider
deploying the troops we are carrying, but there is little light
left and our primary task is at first light the next morning and

timed from Malapati, so we give the area a good hosing down, mark the position for trackers to carry out a follow-up the next morning and continue to our jumping-off point. Lucky boys on the ground, but at least it has got everybody's blood up.

The camp attack follows the normal routine of a Canberra alpha bomb attack, followed by Hunters taking out the flak positions and then a vertical envelopment by our heliborne troops. There are no paratroops as the Dakotas are supporting another raid elsewhere.

I am flying with John Dawson, no relation to Mark, who is the OC of 2 Commando, whose troops are on the ground. John is a sickeningly good-looking officer, who is one of those people who, whatever they're doing, never seem to have a hair out of place or a smudge of dirt on their clothes. I used to play rugby with a guy like it, who, like John, wasn't frightened of getting stuck in, but just seemed to step out of it looking like a film star. He is one of the operators I like flying with in the K-Car, and so is his second in command Andy Samuels, who is flying with Mark in the other gunship; I've been in several successful deployments with the both of them.

John had kept me amused the night before with a story of two sticks of his troops who'd cornered a gook armed with a nRPD in a cave. There was little help the gunship could directly give, and the young subaltern was going to assault the cave after initiating the attack with a white phosphorous rifle grenade. John saw the white smoke from the grenade detonation and his troops charge the position, and was then astounded to see them about turn and retreat down the hill being chased by a lone terrorist waving his machine gun. He can't get his young officer on the radio, the gunship can't fire into the melee, and eventually they all disappear into thick bush.

Radio comms are finally made and John is furious that Rhodesia's finest have been routed. The poor subbie, who is gasping out his explanation whilst panting for breath, finally gets his story over. The grenade had hit a wasps' nest, and that marked the end of the war for everybody involved. They are all seriously stung, especially the terrorist, who was 'arrested' and is now a prisoner, when one of the troopies notices him running alongside them down the hill.

The air strikes go in and we get the troops down and start the sweep into the camp. It turns out that the camp is longer than planned for, and only half has been bombed. The enemy gets themselves organised, and the sweep line starts getting into some heavy resistance; we are taking a lot of small arms fire and then some interest from a 12.7 that we can't locate. I notice the other gunship is orbiting very wide of the camp area and call him in closer. Mark says that we seem to be taking a lot of fire and he wants to stay away from it. It's a very sensible attitude but that's not what we're paid for, and so I invite him over to try to divide the flak between us. He gets into the same orbit, but it has little effect; the enemy has decided it doesn't like our particular aircraft and continues to use us as their target. At the end of the day we have twenty-odd holes in the machine and the other K-Car isn't marked.

Now the troops have taken a casualty and I call in one of the troopers to carry out a casevac in the camp area. The eastern half of the camp is cleared, but there is some pretty stiff resistance being offered by the terrorists left in the western part. Ian Peacock arrives in the casevac area and I get him into a wide low-level orbit of the camp whilst briefing him on the ground picture. I call for the stick with the casualty to pop a smoke, and once he has confirmed that he is visual with the LZ location to plan his approach into it in his own time, but to let me know when he is on short finals and again before he lifts off. I tell him to approach from the east as there are still enemy to the west and when he lifts off, to turn a 180 in the LZ and exit the way he came in.

We continue searching for the 12.7, and it is about a minute later when a ground callsign shouts to us that a helicopter is hovering right over the enemy. I look down and see Ian in a very slow approach low over the trees from the west – he's right over the enemy's position. He continues into the LZ. We have some terse exchanges over the radio; he's just got completely befuddled in the confusing environment of his first punch-up. Amazingly, he hasn't taken a hit or even been aware that he was fired at. He apologises profusely, and as I am telling him to take care on the exit the inevitable happens, and we watch in disbelief as he lifts into a hover, does a 180 and hover taxis out the same way as he came in, back over the enemy. This time he does squawk that he's being fired at. He seems to be clear so I call:

"When you crash, just set fire to the wreckage so we'll all have a marker for the gooks."

He comes out undamaged and I tell him to go straight to the hospital at Buffalo Range. At that moment, there is a series of explosions in the area of the casevac. The gooks are mortaring back into their own position. John and I do a quick ground appreciation, and as another salvo comes down, agree that the most likely position is from the only area of high ground nearby. There is a small hill about a thousand metres south-west of the camp, and we start towards it with Finch briefed to smother it with 20mm as soon as he can bring the gun to bear.

We are about thirty seconds from the hill when a ground callsign tells us they are being fired at by the 12.7. I have an idea of the rough area where the gun is and automatically look there. I see the muzzle flashes and rack the aircraft towards it. Finch has been looking at the hill and doesn't see it, but I get him to put a burst on the ground, and with two quick corrections he is right on the target and we finally silence the thing.

As we are turning I catch a flash on the horizon to the south of us, deep into Mocambique. My first thought is that it is a Mocambiquan ground attack fighter coming to spoil our day, but then I see that it is in fact a helicopter. Strange – and then I have a sudden worry. I call Ian Peacock and ask him to turn on his rotating beacon.

Shortly after there is a flashing red light from the mystery helicopter. Slowly and calmly I tell him to turn off his beacon, do a 180 – the poor chap has been doing them all afternoon – and fly north back towards Rhodesia. We watch the lonesome dot start back towards us and keep an eye on it until it passes by on its way north. The mortaring hasn't continued, and after silencing the 12.7 the sweep through the camp is easily managed.

There is a sequel to the story. After the war I am talking with a ZANLA commander who relates an episode where he escaped from an attack on one of their forward bases, and paused with his group to lob six mortar bombs back into the camp. I get him to sketch the camp layout and the position of the tube when they fired. It was Rio, and after telling him he was about twenty seconds from getting a full load of twenty mill unload on him, he recalled that there was a helicopter coming towards them, but it turned away before getting there. We have a full and frank exchange of beers and a good laugh.

As things stabilise in the camp, the troops are searching the area and the G-Cars are lifting out various booty in the form of documents and captured weaponry, I decide I'd like to take some photos from the air. I crew up into the helicopter flown by Bill Michie, replacing his gunner as he goes into the camp area on a routine resupply task. Bill is known to his course mates as 'Bill of a thousand questions', and I briefly remember an incident during the day when I was talking him onto an LZ and asked him to turn right, whereupon he wanted to know why not go left – no particular reason, that was just the way I was trying to sequence him out of the way of the next helo I was going to talk-on, just a little annoying.

We get into the camp area and I start snapping away. But Sod is still in the area laying down the law, and a contact develops with some gooks that have remained hidden in the area. A circus act develops where I am trying to fire the twin Brownings whilst Bill is cavorting around the area and keeps taking us directly over the top of the gooks. The situation is eventually resolved in our favour, but it scares me senseless and makes me realise how vulnerable our gunners are in these situations, and how reliant they are on a pilot who has the ground picture in his head.

We finally get back to Buffalo Range and have a fairly extensive debrief. I allude several times to the day's similarity to trying to keep control of a litter of gambolling puppies, but the truth is these youngsters have performed exceptionally well in their first contact. Nobody who hasn't been there will fully appreciate the absolute confusion and lack of comprehension in the chaos of any combat, let alone your first airborne one, or appreciate how disorienting it is. Some of them weren't even sure if they were authorised to open fire, which seems at first sight astounding, but it was perhaps something we had taken for granted and I certainly made a point of clearing in future briefings with new boys.

Good people, who all went on to become good operators – Mark Dawson, Pete Le Roux, Ian Peacock, Bill Michie, Roger Thomas, Chas Goatley.

★

This develops into a successful tour, with a series of successful contacts, including a memorable day when we had three separate hundred percent kill rate punch-ups, albeit against groups of two to four, before breakfast. We watch an incredible display of aggression by the RLI at the culmination of the last of these. We catch two out in the open and Finch kills one and wounds the other with a couple of bursts, but the survivor, armed with an RPD, gets into cover under the bank in a bend of dry watercourse, where we can't bring effective fire to bear. The stick that has been dropped closest is directed towards his position. They are coming up in ground with little cover, and are moving up a slight incline. We are just warning them to stay alert as they are coming out of dead ground from the gook, when we see the bullet strikes from the RPD in amongst them. There is no hesitation or thought of taking cover; they turn straight into the line of fire and charge the position, firing on the run, the machine gunner from the hip. The matter is swiftly concluded. John informs me that they are his youngest stick, all just out of training and eighteen years old.

Along with our new pilots, we have also had an influx of young technician/gunners, and some of them are very good. Some of the older flight sergeants are, of course, excellent gunners; I enjoy operating with Alan Aird, John Britton, Jenkie, Paul Braun and Peter McCabe, who are all excellent shots, as well as Hajj and Mufti Upton. McCabe shows me an amazing trick for lifting a full fuel drum on top of another to assist in refuelling, but I can never remember the cat's cradle you have to make with your arms before rotating it. However, there is an element of the 'old guard' on the squadron who are living on past events that occurred when the terrorists hadn't learnt either to take cover from the helicopters or to shoot accurately at them, which they certainly have now.

We are scrambled one afternoon, and Finch, who is having a dose of the trots, is otherwise engaged. I brief one of the G-Car pilots to either wait for him or get somebody else from the ops room to sit behind his gun and catch us up, and grab a young gunner, Eduardo Crivellari, and tell him to man the cannon in the K-Car. He says he's not qualified on the gun, but I tell him to jump in anyway, so it is unreasonable of me to get pissed off when he tells me after we're airborne that the barrel is not connected. I tell him to get it fixed, which is perfectly acceptable, but involves some hair-raising antics leaning outside the aircraft whilst connected to the monkey chain to locate the barrel and lock it into the mounting. The poor little bugger finally gets it done and then I tell him to get outside again and positively make sure it is locked in position – Mufti famously didn't on one occasion, and his first round fired took the barrel with it. Knowing his luck, it probably speared somebody to death.

We arrive at the scene of the sighting, drop some sticks and Andy Samuels, who is the commando officer flying with us, starts organising the sweeps. It is an extremely hot afternoon, and after an hour they have found no sign whatever of any presence. We are coming around to making the decision to call it a day, when I hear a single round close to the aircraft. Unless they hit you, to hear them means they are generally under the rotor disc. Andy and Criv say they hadn't heard it, and enquiries of the troops on the ground also prove negative, but they may have been blanketed by the noise of the chopper overheard. I convince Andy that I am sure it was a round, and he gets the troops sweeping again. I can tell from the radio responses that they are distinctly unchuffed at this exercise. Another half an hour goes by and I see a gook sitting with his back against a baobab tree. The whole area is as flat as can be, covered in bush and baobabs, so there are no distinguishing features. I daren't take my eyes of the sighting and tell Criv to pick the gun up and squeeze off a short burst. He wants to know what at, and I tell him I just want to see a mark on the ground.

"OK. From your last strike, go left four hundred." It is a massive correction, but he duly puts another burst down.

"Add 50 from that… Now fire at the base of the baobab ten to the left."

The final burst goes down, and I tell him to make the gun safe and cradle it. He thinks I've gone mad. Andy is also looking at me strangely as the troops are going haywire on the radio asking what's going on, and asks:

"Sir, what was that all about?"

"Congratulations, Criv, you've just killed your first gook."

Sure enough, a stick sweeps into the area and finds a dead terrorist. He is older than the average and his weapon is a really well-used SKS rather than the more usual AK – it has recently been fired – big mistake.

It has probably cost nearly a hundred thousand dollars to kill this poor unfortunate, and I look back on it today with regret and amazement that I still thought our leaders were serious in prosecuting the war to win it, to justify it.

Along with Beaver Shaw, John Jacobs, Mark Furnell and Mark Jackson, Crivellari becomes one of the aces on the gun.

★

The fireforce is reduced to one plus three, although we are left a spare K-Car – along with fireforce duties we are covering an SAS external deployment down the railway line, and the spare is stripped out of the army officer's armoured seat and other odds and ends so we can carry extra fuel and ammunition. There is also a change of gunners; John Britton takes over from Finch, and 2 Commando are replaced by an independent company as the ground element, with Captain John MacDonald as their boss.

We are on standby on int that a Grey Scouts unit is tracking a group of twenty-five that are marching a hundred-odd recruits south towards the border for training in Mocambique.

The Grey Scouts are a mounted infantry unit that has a niche role particularly in the flatlands of the lowveld here – apparently the horses are very quiet in the bush, obviously cover ground much faster than men and the animal smell is not alien in the bush, as are various human odours.

When they finally call for us, they are unsure of their gridref. The briefing officers are getting umpty with them about this, but I'd rather they were honest than manufacture a grid just to satisfy the callout requirements, which state a six-figure reference for both themselves and the enemy. I'd rather have a less accurate reference, but know that the location is definitely within those parameters rather than an inaccurate six figure, as I believe it is a matter of focusing on the right area. I am sure we have missed many, many kills in the all-important first minute of arriving at a scene because the grid has been slightly wrong, and the gooks who were in fact in the periphery of our vision as we arrived were able to snivel away before we get the position rectified, but my argument has been dismissed.

Goodness knows how these guys on the ground map-read in this terrain anyway; it's difficult enough from the air, where we can obviously see a wider area and more features, and triangulate with high ground on the horizon. I am happy with the general area and ask that as soon as the ground callsign hear us they must throw smoke. My theory is that if our own troops can hear us, so can the enemy, who will start to take evasive action, and with the smoke visual we at least have a direct bearing and distance to their last known location. The Grey Scouts are very close to these guys anyway, who appear to be taking an extended rest in the heat of the day.

I am just starting to flap there has been a snafu as, calculating by flying time and heading, I think they should have heard us by now, when the cry "Contact, contact" comes over the radio, and there is a great plume of white phosphorous smoke almost directly below us. Conditions have favoured us and our approach has not only been undetected, we have arrived at the exact position of the Greys. I look ahead on the bearing to the gooks and we're immediately visual and John has got the gun going. A fearsome fusillade of automatic small arms is directed towards us, and we take a massive hit in the cockpit which shatters the radios.

We end up with intercom between JB and me and I seem to be able to transmit, although JB is having to relay the answers to me – MacDonald is off the air on both receive and transmit. There is a fierce air-to-ground exchange of fire for several minutes until we get the position stabilised. I use the word reservedly; there are no obviously armed gooks running around, but a lot of denim-clad recruits rushing about, obviously scared witless and not having the knowledge to take cover. Paradoxically, this is probably keeping them alive – if they're not armed and wearing blue overalls we are not specifically targeting them. However, added to this there is a posse of riderless horses charging around the battlefield. The Greys' mounts are trained to work in the proximity of automatic small arms fire, but this is the first time they have heard the K-Car working and they are truly spooked. Amazingly, also, there are a number of Dalek-like vehicles trundling around – unbeknown to any of the other participants in this joust, an armoured car unit had been listening in and on hearing the word 'contact' came flying into the area unannounced and started waving their ninety mills around. It is the most incredible scene from above and, with the limited radio control we have, it takes some time to get squared away. We are out of ammunition, have inadequate radio comms and other damage, so I leave a G-Car in command and strict instructions not to start moving troops until we return – the armoured cars have finally been brought onto a compatible frequency and told to regroup as a stop line some distance back from the main contact area. We then depart for Buffalo Range who have been instructed to get the GT model K-Car ready for immediate crew change and departure when we arrive.

This is duly accomplished, but I have sort of forgotten that John Mac is completely mystified as to what is going and am slightly surprised to see him running alongside as we start to taxi in the second machine, shouting at JB.

"Sir, he wants to know where he can sit."

"Ask him, does he want to come?"

"Sir, yes he does, sir."

"OK. Tell him he'll have to sit on the floor with his feet on the step outside."

We get airborne and I notice there is a long and involved conversation between the two of them about where to plug in his intercom lead – there isn't anywhere – and then we're back at the scene. We get the troops sweeping and there are several more heated ground-to-air exchanges and many more ground contacts, but we have an excellent day and account for all the gooks, without too many of the recruits being killed or injured. The survivors have all, for sure, been converted to the security forces' way of life. It takes three days to round up all the horses that have gone awol, and at one point we even task a spotter fixed-wing to assist.

We celebrate with a good shebeen in Buffalo Range's great

bar; the 'indep' troops are cock-a-hoop, as they rarely get into fireforce punch-ups, and the Grey Scouts and armoured car units are also chuffed and even sit down to iron out their co-ordination problems.

MacDonald is less than chuffed, though, with JB's explanation as to why he was allowed on board in the second gunship when he knew there was no intercom or armoured seat for him. John tells him:

"Mister Borlace did ask me to ask you if you wanted to come, sir, and you said "yes.""

"But there was no radio for me."

"Sir, you said you wanted to come."

"But I don't understand why."

"Sir, we fly in a left-hand orbit. The bullets come up from the left. If you want to sit between where they're coming from and my pilot, we're both more than happy for you to do so."

He's not sure whether it's a joke or not. On reflection, neither am I.

CHAPTER SEVENTEEN

Headquarters – Again

I return from a few days off to find the door of my room at the officers' single quarters has been battered off its hinges and several items are missing from my personal kit, most noticeably my survival belt complete with 9mm automatic pistol and my personal weapon, which is an AK47. It is advocated that we carry an FN rifle, which is the standard weapon of the security forces, but it is too long to fit easily to hand near the pilot's seat. Several pilots have been shot down into the middle of ongoing contacts, including myself, and the last thing you need is to be faffing around getting your weapons out of the aircraft – the one person soldiers on the ground would love to meet is the chap who has been strafing them.

One of the South Africans who was RPGed in an LZ debussed and took cover behind a baobab tree, which in his own words was a couple of strides away – it turned out that it was nearly a hundred metres from his burning aircraft. My philosophy is to depart the aircraft and to create as much confusion and noise as possible whilst I am getting into cover, where I can sort myself out for Custer's last stand and squawk for help on the survival beacon. To this end, I have the folding butt AK, which is as short as a sub-machine gun with the stock folded. I had previously carried a nasty little Czech-made SMG that all the fundis advised against, but it fulfilled my criteria; the magazine carried lots of bullets, it never jammed, and it took offence and went off if you so much as looked at it the wrong way. To criticism that its effective range was only twenty-five yards, I answered that as far as I was concerned, if somebody was more than twenty-five yards away, he wasn't in my personal space, and if he went his way, I'd go mine. I'd also experimented with the Israeli Uzi. It is a lovely weapon, but has to be continually cleaned, and has three separate safety features to prevent negligent discharges, before the bad news starts coming out of the sharp end. For me, that is three too many when you're having a bad hair day.

The AK is ideal – it carries lots of bullets, they are more powerful than the subs, and it is short-barrelled enough to lay right beside my seat ready to be grabbed as you are exiting the aircraft. It also has the benefit of being made for use by peasants and fires no matter how dirty or dusty it is. I have two magazines taped together, which is not recommended normally because the breech is not designed for that sort of strain, but I figure I want it for one-time use. The first magazine has a mix all the way down of tracer alternating with armour-piercing and my plan is to just pull the trigger as I am demonstrating discretion being the better part of valour, high-stepping away from the field of battle, making a lot of noise and green and red fireworks. I keep it in the cockpit with a round up the spout and safety off, and am constantly being told that this is unsafe, which is exactly what I want to hear. I do not want to carry a safe weapon. One of my regular gunners is Mufti Upton, who had previously served with the RLI. Although he disdains my choice of weapon, preferring the FN, he teaches me the most important thing to do before dismantling and cleaning it – check the serial number, to make sure you're not cleaning somebody else's.

Vic Cook has recently been shot down whilst carrying out a casevac, and literally crashed into the middle of the terrorist group – several were hit by the blades and flying wreckage. His

Uzi is also not fireable, but he disarms and shoots a gook and then uses the captured AK to carry out a single-handed contact with the survivors and get Finch Bellringer, his gunner, who has been shot several times, and the casualty into cover, and then hold off several counter-attacks until the cavalry arrives. He earns a well-deserved Silver Cross.

*

I call the guardroom to report the break-in to my cabin and they tell me they are fully aware of the incident and I am to call my squadron commander immediately. He has recently taken over, and we have crossed swords in the past a couple of times. He is in no need of an explanation and tells me that the burglary was in fact the Air Force Police 'acting on information received' and I am to present myself to Air Headquarters first thing tomorrow morning in my best bib and tucker, where I will be charged with various firearms offences.

I duly present myself, and Terry Emsley marches me in front of the director general of operations, the avuncular 'KAS' Edwards. He runs through a litany of offences, which include keeping weapons unsecured, having a pistol, the property of the state, in an unclean condition, and carrying communist weapons of war. He is obviously as pissed off with having to deal with this nonsense as I am at being there, says he is going to deal with the matter summarily and asks if I will accept his punishment. I say "no thanks" and elect to be tried by court-martial. There is a stunned silence. He tells the airman who has been recording the proceedings to leave the room, and we have an 'off-the-record' clearing of the air.

He explains that this is not a serious matter and they just want to get it out of the way quickly. I say that as far as I am concerned it is serious, and I am distinctly unchuffed about having my door demolished and kit rifled. We are on a heavily guarded military airfield; like all of the helicopter pilots I am effectively available for call out at any hour of the day or night, and I consider that my survival kit and weapons are perfectly secure in a locked cupboard in a locked room. The only time they have been interfered with in three years has been this incident, when for some reason the station police have felt it necessary to bull the door off its hinges and ransack my cabin.

He agrees that there appears to be no justification for the drastic action that has been carried out, and that as an entirely separate matter the people who instigated it have been reprimanded, but the fact remains that once these charges have been brought they have to be dealt with. There can be no excuse for the unclean state of my pistol, and why was it in such a state?

Coincidentally, a week previously we had a pistol shooting competition in the bush, and mine was the only automatic that didn't jam, but my explanation that the reason it was in that condition was "because, sir, it has been living in the same shit conditions in the bush as its owner", although causing Emsley to start laughing aloud, isn't appreciated from the other side of the desk.

He asks why I want to go to court-martial – which is every officer's right – and I tell him that if the air force can afford to waste time on this sort of crap, which, whatever the verdict, will be a public embarrassment if it goes to a court martial, whilst we are spending weeks at a time on continuous operations in the bush, then I am quite willing to spend six weeks without being shot at whilst all the various evidence and statements are compiled, and am quite confident that Prof Christie will defend me successfully. The mention of Prof Christie, Dean of Law at the University, and a reserve captain on 3 Squadron, who is always ready to jump in and defend the misdemeanours of aircrew when the air force gets snotty, causes a sucking of teeth. After a big external, Peinke, Delport and Willie Knight have a heated confrontation with Barney Barnes, the station warrant officer from Sarum who is running the jump-off camp at Darwin, about waking up the camp with gravel on the wriggly tin roofs and raucous singing to celebrate their return to an environment without flak, where they have spent the last couple of days. Barney unfortunately has a heart attack during the night and dies. The air force decides they are going to charge the three pilots with manslaughter. Prof Christie gets involved and the charges are quickly forgotten about.

KAS tells Emsley to march me out, talk some sense into me and to come back in thirty minutes. We sit in Terry's office with coffee, and although he is highly amused at the proceedings, he counsels not to play hardball as the air force are just looking for a face-saving exit out of this situation, but that they will not back off – I have to plead guilty.

We march back in and recommence the charade. I stick by the decision for a court martial. Edwards again halts the proceedings, and gives me another reading of my fortune, delivered in a less avuncular style. He points out that there is no possible defence to the charge of carrying a communist weapon of war, and that the law provides for the death sentence for its transgression. He goes on to remind me that the whole exercise is intrinsically not important, why don't I plead guilty, he'll fine me and that'll be the end of the matter?

"Sir, you've just threatened me with the death penalty. That's pretty important in my book. If you want to go ahead with this fiasco, so do I. As it happens, the weapon is not a communist weapon of war and if you want to put one of your front-line airframe drivers on trial, good luck with getting the rest to stick their cocks on the block so readily."

"What do you mean it's not communist? Of course it bloody well is!"

Voices are being raised on both sides of the table.

"In fact, sir, it is the property of the South African government, and was given to me as a bonsella by One Recce after Goatley and I got our arses shot off pulling their guys out of the shit down the railway line whilst they were here doing ops on our behalf in Mocambique – and that will be my defence."

There is a stunned silence.

"You can't say that – it's top secret."

"Try me. I'm happy to go and get shot at just about every day. I spend most of my life in the bush whilst people are swanning around here worrying about their bridge schools and sports' afternoon – but I am not performing in this sort of farce. Sir."

There is a long silence.

"Emsley. Get him out of here. And I want you both back here at two o' clock, when we'll all have calmed down and it'll be dealt with."

Terry and I adjourn to his office down the corridor.

"Jesus, Mike. Don't push it."

"He's only stopped now because its lunch time and he wants to get a few hands of bridge in." That's unfair of me; he has got a war to run apart from dealing with this sort of nonsense, but I am really hacked off by now.

"I'm going for some beer; I'll be back before two."

Terry is worried firstly that I won't come back, and secondly that I will come back, but pissed. He offers to come with me to make sure that neither occurs, but I reassure him on both counts and say that I am going to meet with someone. I borrow his phone and arrange to meet for a piri-piri chicken lunch in a Portuguese restaurant in the avenues.

We duly march back in at about two-thirty. KAS looks up as we stop, and with no preamble announces:

"All the charges are dropped, other than the dirty pistol. You're fined forty dollars. Dismissed."

We about turn and march out. Even I know when to call it a day.

So does Emsley. He lends me a civvy jacket, changes himself into a set of dog robbers he keeps in his office and we retire to the Red Fox to be out of the orbit of headquarters, spending the rest of the day getting snot-gobbling drunk before returning to New Sarum for the Friday night prayers meeting. The rumour mill is running hot about my fate, and we are able to bring the crowd up to date with the outcome, the story having already been polished and embellished in several details, particularly in regard to highly exaggerated dire threats of the gallows and Emsley's personal delight of the pistol living in the shit like its owner.

★

At this stage of the war, the South Africans were developing their reconnaissance commando units. Several individuals had been up operating with the SAS and Scouts, but in 1977 they deployed One Recce to Mahabauluta to operate autonomously on mine-laying, reconnaissance and fighting patrols in Mocambique. There is a small C Squadron advisory team led by Mick Graham attached to them and a couple of helos for hot extraction and casevac duties.

The deployment does not go off as smoothly as our special forces exercises do – these guys are doing it for the first time. Several times we are called to hot extract teams that have literally just been deployed – including one occasion when we had been reinforced by the Chiredzi fireforce to deploy a fighting patrol down near Mapai, and as we landed were told to refuel and get back down there to extract them as they were screeching about having been compromised.

The gift of the South African manufactured AK came about after a patrol way down the line called for an extraction of some wounded after being bumped. They assured us they had broken contact and had moved to a secure LZ at least ten clicks from the railway. As we got close and they started talking us onto their loc, it became obvious that they were very, very close to the line. Fuel on these sorties was always absolutely marginal, so there was never any time for fannying about – they assured me that there were no Freds around and so I made the decision to go in to them. Almost inevitably, their LZ was ambushed; the Freds had realised what was likely to occur and had held off springing the trap until the choppers landed – the commandos had obviously not even sent out a clearance patrol. We had a situation where thirty soldiers were trying to get aboard two Alouettes, and there were choice exchanges on the radio until we got airborne with the three wounded. We took a snottie exiting the LZ, and told the patrol commander to break contact and get himself well to the east from where I'd arrange a full fireforce to come and get them the following morning soon after first light – an exercise which went off without hitch.

Mick Graham had had enough; all the deployed callsigns were extracted and he held a briefing explaining to them in unequivocal terms that their job was to make contact with the enemy and harass him; being shot at was not in itself a cause for extraction.

Their commander, Charles Nordee, gave them the same words in Afrikaans, sounding rather more forceful, and subsequently, and as their confidence built, they began to operate more aggressively. When the front line came to their own borders with Mocambique and Angola, some years later, the recces proved to be very able and aggressive cross-border operators.

CHAPTER EIGHTEEN

Kavalamanja

The siren wails and we start the routine for another fireforce callout from Mtoko. I go straight to the ops room, receive the gen from the army intelligence officer and am ready to brief the fireforce pilots when they have all arrived. The briefing is short, covering the gridref, the details of the callout – in this case, it is a Scouts OP that has a group of twenty-five plus visual on a rock kopje – radio frequencies are confirmed, the location of the nearest fuel, any reserve troops for a helicopter second wave, and then we trot towards the aircraft on the hard standing. Meanwhile the techs have gone straight to the aircraft and made sure they are ready to go. I always authorise mine to have the engine going, so I can hop in and just have to get strapped in and the radios on whilst engaging the rotors. Depending on how far the initial run is, I will get them to add more fuel. Some K-Car drivers permanently have a couple of hours' worth of fuel onboard. I prefer to keep my aircraft lighter, with about twenty minutes' worth more fuel than the troopers – on the basis that if we get into an immediate punch-up, the gunship is more manoeuvrable and can lay down fire more effectively; the lead G-Car can drop his stick and refuel, then take the army airborne commander to oversee the deployment of the sticks whilst we refuel and rearm, and then we're back on station to provide top cover for the troops' sweep into the target area. I also, somewhat unusually, keep my aircraft parked at the back of the formation so that I am visual with the troopers and see that they are loaded and ready to taxi, rather than relying on radio calls, before calling for take-off and then taxiing past them to get the formation sequenced correctly.

This gridref is reasonably close and when we arrive there is a good talk-on by a black Scouts operator. My normal procedure is to tell him that I am going to drop a smoke generator on the indicated target as I understand it and then they are to direct me from the smoke, rather than the old method where they had been taught to try and direct the aircraft overhead the target, with all its attendant parallax errors. I am just approaching the feature, which is a granite kopje with a cleft gashed through it, when he excitedly calls

"You are overhead the position! You are overhead the position!"

This means that the gridref we have been given is slightly in error, which is quite common and understandable as they often have to come up with a reference estimated from their own position, which can be offset by some kilometres. It is drummed into them that they have to give a six-figure grid reference, and I have tried to advocate a change that this is fine if they are absolutely certain this is the exact location of the terrs, but otherwise it is better to give us a four figure grid – a one kilometre square – in which the group is located if they are not able to give the exact co-ordinates, and we are not then focused on just one place.

As the call comes through the earphones there is a concentrated burst of automatic small arms fire and a big clang somewhere behind us in the fuselage. The smoke goes anyway, and I turn hard and see the gooks in the cleft. Good cover for a ground battle, but it is a bit like being in a tank once it is under attack; they are now trapped in this natural fortress and this fight will be their last. Jenkie gives the area a working over with the 20mm whilst we get the helicopter troops on the ground as stop groups in natural escape avenues, then the paratroops drop from the Dakota and organise into a sweep line to assault the position. I send one of the G-Cars to nearby Kotwa to refuel to full and wait on the ground for me, organise the Lynx to put his two frans into the cleft in the rocks, setting the undergrowth alight, and Freddy Watts, the army commander, gets his sweep line moving towards the brick, before I astonish him by breaking hard off to the right and autorotating towards Kotwa. I have been watching the fuel gauge visibly decreasing as all this has been going on; the clang at the start of the contact was obviously in the fuel tank and it has been badly holed as the fuel is pouring out – there is just about enough to get us on the ground at Kotwa. I tell Freddy that we are no longer part of this battle, but he is to jump out and use the fully refuelled G-Car as a command ship to direct his troops.

Sure enough, inspection by Jenkie and the other techs confirms a big chunk out of the tank. They are self-sealing, but the bullet must have been tumbling and it has taken a corner off the tank. They plug the tank as best they can and we refuel to full and set off for Salisbury which we reach several hours later having had to refuel to full twice on the way, due to the fuel leaking out so badly.

Signals have been sent ahead and there is a replacement aircraft waiting for us when we get to the squadron. It is not quite ready, they are finishing a primary servicing or something, and whilst we are waiting I notice a modified armoured seat standing in the corner of the hangar. At this stage of the war, the pilots, and in the gunship the gunners and army commander, are protected by fully armoured seats that have high sides to protect the thighs and extensions that protect either side of the head as well as full armour at the rear and the back of the head. They offer pretty good protection to all but your lower legs – Danny Svoboda reckons that at the first sound of gunfire he just lifts his legs onto the seat and adopts the yoga lotus position which has the treble benefits of relaxing him in a time of high stress, protecting his legs and confusing the enemy gunners as the chopper spins with no yaw control – and the left side of the body, as your left arm has to be free to move the collective.

The new modification is a bracket extending out from the seat to support a plate of armour outboard of your left arm and providing cover for bullets coming up towards you from the left. It is rather like a smaller version of the shields carried by knights of old, and quickly becomes known as the heart shield. Geoff Dartnall tells me it is the only one on the squadron at the moment; they have just finished the trials and it has been cleared for operational use. I ask him to fit it on our aircraft. Initially he thinks I'm joking, but it is not doing any good in the hangar, and it may as well be on our aircraft as anyone's, so it gets fitted and we return to Mtoko to listen to the war stories about the punch-up in the morning. I also have to hand my K-Car with its new shield over to Ted Lunt as there is a signal ordering two G-Cars to detach for Mangula, with specifically myself to take one of them. Ted and I do a straight swap, and I go off with his gunner Hansie Steyn in the morning. I assume it is to provide a hot-extraction facility for some special forces operation in Zambia, but when we arrive it is to join a gathering of over a dozen helicopters, a couple of Lynxes and three Dakotas. There is obviously a raid on.

★

There are three gunships and ten G-Cars. The sequence of events is going to be Hunters followed by Canberras, with our gunships covering the subsequent heli assault and the paradrop. I am sitting at the back quietly crowing with Ken Newman that for once we are going to be Yellow Ten or something right at the back and ferrying troops, whilst he and the other K-Cars are jousting.

We have a new squadron commander though, old friend Grimshag, and after he gives us the ra-ra talk that has to be added after all the important parts of the briefing have been covered, he drops his bombshell. As the 'new boy' he doesn't want to prejudice the timing or execution of this strike with any snafus, so our formation will be led by me who has to swap aircraft again, followed by 'Gaps'. He is also worried about the possibility of strong opposition from the camp – well ,hallelujah – so the G-Cars will come next with the protection of himself in the third gunship at the back. This idea is so novel that everybody is stunned into acquiescent silence, and before we know where we are the briefing is over. 'Follow me men, I'll be right behind you!'

The strike is initially delayed due to bad weather but finally goes in and the revised timings all go to plan. The Hunters take out the heavy anti-aircraft artillery as it has been plotted by Schulie and Martin and marked on our target air photos, and apart from the ubiquitous automatic small arms fire we have a pretty easy time of it, although several strellas are fired at both us and the Hunters. The helicopters have pretty good anti-strella protection; they have been modified with a shroud that deflects the hot exhaust gas stream up into the rotors. Experiments show that there is actually more infrared emission from the Plexiglas canopy than our exhaust, and on either seeing a launch, which is very distinctive, showing a loop of white smoke as it comes out of the launcher, or hearing the call "Strella, strella", we immediately drop the collective, thereby decreasing power and thus drastically lowering the exhaust temperature, as well as rapidly moving us in two planes away from where we had been. The Hunters, however, have to rely on either outrunning them or fooling the seeker heads into acquiring a more attractive target like the sun. On a different external raid, Dave Bourhill collects a spectacular hole in his wing as he turns hard and a missile punches through it.

Unfortunately, a combination of thick jessie bush and flooded land slows the troops' advance and it takes them too long to get into the camp; a lot of the occupants have long since departed. By the time the sweep lines are in the camp, we have established a 'cab rank' system of one K-Car on task to supply fire support and a perch for the army commanders to control their troops. For some reason, the tactical command of the troops on this raid is being split between an overall commander, airborne in one of the Lynxes, and Majors Pat Armstrong and Freddy Watts, alternating in the K-Cars. I think the guy in the Lynx's chief task is to Telstar to Salisbury in case there is any severe reaction from the Zambian army, so that the right 'political' decision can be made, as he doesn't seem to be taking too much interest in the fight through of the camp.

I am returning for a stint in the cab rank in the afternoon and can't raise the on-station K-Car for a handover brief. A callsign on the ground comes up on the air; it transpires he is the senior RLI NCO. He tells us that the K-Car has gone to channel five but we had better get in touch with three two alpha who are in serious trouble in square foxtrot two seven on the air photo. We call three two alpha. The poor guy – as it turns out – he is a second lieutenant who has passed out of the School of Infantry less than two weeks previously, has one man dead, another wounded and is pinned down by a 12.7mm machine gun in a bunker. They are in cover, but their slightest movement attracts a big slap from the bunker. We tell him to calm down and standby and I change channels and raise our new boss, who should be giving this guy top cover. He is supervising the recovery of parachutes from the original DZ by two G-Cars and a couple of sticks. Yes, he had been called by three two alpha, but his assessment was that there was no assistance he could give as they were within the safety distance for the 20mm and the enemy was in a bunker anyway. He has told them to withdraw to a safe distance and then he'll call for a frantan or rocket strike. Freddy is about to go ballistic with rage, but I change frequencies quickly and motion to him to cool down; we'll sort it out.

We get the callsign on the ground to get his two flanking soldiers to pop a smoke grenade in a position that confirms to us that everybody is east of a line drawn between the two smokes. We can't see the bunker from the air and ask if they can lob a white phos onto it, but at this stage they have none left. We orbit a couple of times and I spend a long time talking with Hans – if what I think is the bunker is correct, they are very close to it indeed. We tell them to keep their heads down and we will fire a couple of rounds onto what we think is the target. Waiting until we are firing from behind our own troops' position, Hans puts down a two-round burst exactly on the position I want, and the subbie confirms that this is the bunker opening but that the rounds had exploded outside as there is a significant overhang. We explain that we are going to put in a sustained burst on this same position and he is to withdraw under its cover, taking the wounded man with him but leaving the dead guy behind for the time being. We will not be giving any 'go' orders from above; as soon as the firing starts he is to make his move and we will keep it up for as long as we can. Now he must let us know when his troops are briefed and ready. I have another long chat with Hans. I am going to come to a high hover in a position where he can fire over the heads of our troops into the mouth of the bunker and he is to fire on the exact position as before – not in a series of bursts but in one long sustained burst; I want the occupants fully distracted.

Coming to a high hover is not a recommended practice; generally we wouldn't have the power for a free air hover anyway, but you are also of course providing a static target for anybody on the ground. As it is, we don't have enough power to hold the hover but we are descending slowly and slightly forwards and Hansie puts in about a ten-second sustained burst. We cease fire only because the recoil from the gun is causing the helicopter to roll so much he cannot keep on the target. His shooting is immaculate and a great cloud of dust obscures the bunker mouth. Shortly afterwards, we get a grateful call from the extricated callsign, and by and by one of the Lynxes puts his frans just short of the mouth, which is exactly the right place for the burning gel to fly forward into the bunker and spoil everybody's day in there.

During the wash-up of the strike, the word 'cowardice' is mentioned privately to one of the senior officers with regard to the disgraceful behaviour of the other gunship, but he persuades us that this is not a route that will gain any mileage, so we swap aircraft again late in the afternoon and head back to Mtoko.

I am used to Doris greeting my return enthusiastically, but am slightly surprised at Ted Lunt's ebullient warmth. He insists on pouring copious amounts of beer down my throat and I soon find out why. They have had a callout and contact using the K-Car I had given him, during which a round hits the heart shield smack in the centre, probably saving his life. Jenkie isn't quite so happy; the shrapnel from the strike has peppered his cheek, but he's never been the best-looking lad in the world anyway.

★

I am disappointed in Ted's reaction to an incident later in the same detachment. We are sent to a location towards last light –

it is more than likely a Scouts authentication exercise, we never find out for sure, but get some troops on the ground to check the area out as we all remain in an orbit, as we will be picking them up in about fifteen minutes max unless something develops. The light is getting very dim as a figure comes out of the bush adjacent to the indicated camp area. There is a streak of tracer from a G-Car and the figure falls. It is the RLI lieutenant. He is alive, but with a broken leg; we have had a blue on blue.

At the enquiry, I am disappointed that Ted maintains it is entirely the gunner's fault as he had not given permission to fire. I make a statement to the effect that my gunners are briefed to open fire at will in a contact area if they think they have a target visual – quite often, because they are able to look backwards, they see terrorists emerge from cover after the helicopter has passed overhead, and we have achieved many kills due to this. Ted is quite correct in the actual mechanics of how things should happen, but I think it is inappropriate for combat duties. Keith Rayne, the gunner in question, is treated quite appallingly in my opinion and rifted from flying duties. I continue to confirm with my gunners that they are free to open fire at will once we go live, and if there are any snafus I'll take the can; for Christ's sake, we're not playing netball with these people, we're trying to kill them.

CHAPTER NINETEEN

In Conclusion

The Rhodesian front-line combat forces consisted of the BSAP, the army and the Rhodesian Air Force.

The BSAP, somewhat incongruously named as the British South Africa Police, had been established by the British South Africa Company to put down the original rebellions in 1896. Originally structured as a cavalry unit, it fulfilled all the functions of a police force and, in addition, had a paramilitary role to confront civil disturbance, undertaken by the Police Anti-Terrorist Unit – PATU, and had specialist sections, the most significant of which was Special Branch, whose principal function was intelligence gathering, collation and analysis. Many members of both the conventional police, and particularly the anti-terrorist unit and Special Branch, were black. The police had assumed at an early stage the responsibility for the resolution of the terrorist problem, with the army and air force on call to assist as and when requested. This situation was allowed to continue for a ridiculous length of time, and by the time Combined Operations was formed in 1977 and primary responsibility for dealing with 'the problem' – which all but the people actually exchanging bullets with the enemy in daily ferocious firefights still seemed reluctant to call 'the war' – was relinquished, a situation had been allowed to develop that could never be defeated militarily.

From a military point of view, the war was probably lost at the very beginning of 1975. There was a ceasefire in force whilst the Rhodesian government and the African Nationalist Congress were holding talks. Despite four members of the security forces being murdered whilst this agreement was in place, a ridiculously worded order was promulgated delineating the rules of engagement:

"Shoot all insurgents coming into the country. Under no circumstances may you shoot or take offensive action against any insurgents leaving the country."

Thus, large numbers of terrorists were able to leave the country to be retrained, rearmed and eventually redeployed when the ceasefire was terminated at a time of their masters' choosing.

To compound this incredible display of naiveté, a bold plan put forward by then Major Ron Reid-Daly, the commanding officer of the Selous Scouts, was simultaneously rejected out of hand. Mocambique was in turmoil due to the hasty departure of the Portuguese and in disarray due to there being no organised handover to the new government. His plan had been to establish clandestine bases in depth within Mocambique and infiltrate the terrorist groups with members of his own unit, which would conceivably have disrupted the enemy's base areas in that country to the extent that they would not have been able to regroup and mount offensive operations back into Rhodesia, certainly for very many years, perhaps enough to have achieved a political solution.

The army consisted primarily of two units of special forces, C Squadron of the Special Air Service and the Selous Scouts, a commando unit, the Rhodesian Light Infantry, a mounted infantry unit, the Grey Scouts, conventional infantry, the Rhodesian African Rifles, who also became para qualified, and the usual supporting corps, engineers, signals, medical, service and small artillery and armoured car formations. In addition, there was the Rhodesia Regiment, numerically larger than the regular army but operated as a territorial force. Its members were subject to call-ups as promulgated by the government, and the steadily increasing length of these had severely detrimental effects on both morale and the continuation of normal civil business and manufacturing as it denuded society of young men.

The SAS and RLI were totally white units, whilst the RAR consisted until the very last years of the war of white officers and black other ranks, including some very senior and experienced NCOs. The Selous Scouts was the only totally integrated multiracial unit, although the Grey Scouts had a small number of black troopers. The Rhodesia Regiment was also totally white. National service and a compulsory call-up only applied to the white population, but the Rhodesian African Rifles were inundated with volunteers and able to expand to form a second battalion and start the formation of a third. Towards the end of the war, integrated sticks of white and black soldiers were constituted and confirmed what had been apparent from the PATU, the Police Anti-Terrorist Unit, and the Selous Scouts: that this was an entirely effective and efficient method of operating.

The air force at the time of UDI was configured as a nearly perfectly balanced pocket air force for defensive operations. It consisted of Hunter ground attack fighters, a mix of single and dual seat Vampire fighter bombers, a variety of transport aircraft including DC-3 Dakotas, piston-engined Provost light attack and training aircraft, twin jet engine Canberras, which could be used as bombers or for high-level aerial photo-reconnaissance, and Alouette helicopters.

It had been assumed by the British government that the imposition of sanctions would effectively negate the operational capability of the air force due to specialist spares being unavailable, but the Rhodesians proved to be both adept at circumventing sanctions covertly, and technically innovative in modifying equipment or producing local alternatives to unobtainable spares.

Unfortunately, the air staff had also been vulnerable to the self-congratulatory complacency that permeated the early and middle years of the UDI period. By the time the air force found itself involved in a savage counter-terrorist war, where one of the few absolute advantages to a government is access to aerial support and firepower, it was not only undermanned and inadequately trained in counterinsurgency tactics, but the inventory had been allowed to deteriorate to the point where obsolete aircraft had to be brought out of storage to augment the squadrons, and the only additions had been light aircraft, acquired at immense cost and modified to be used in ground support roles.

At its peak, the total number of pilots was around one hundred and fifty, but these numbers had been made up by recalling a lot of older pilots, generally for transport and training duties, and by an influx of very young and inexperienced pilots as a result of an increase in recruitment and training in the latter years of the war. Let me say that these young men performed excellently, learned quickly when exposed to the initial bewilderment of fast-moving contacts as very low-time pilots, and many became excellent operators and fireforce leaders in their own right.

Rhodesian society in general, and the security forces in particular, were rightly proud of their achievements in negating the effects of sanctions and combating the early years of guerrilla activity. However, they had allowed this to develop into a somewhat complacent pomposity that they could handle anything thrown at them using the absolute minimum of resources, and had become an insular and xenophobic society, intolerant of new ideas. There was also a large measure of a sort of schizophrenia; on the one hand everybody enjoyed being associated with some of the truly incredible accomplishments and bravery of those fighting the war, whereas on the other it seemed to be almost a side-show to the business of running a 'real' air force, and the re-establishment of a normal society. During 1976 and 1977, before the benefit of training higher numbers of aircrew started to filter through, the pilots on the two bush squadrons were being pushed to the limits of physical and mental endurance. At times, helicopter aircrew were spending periods of over six weeks on continuous operations, followed by a break of just four days in Salisbury, one of which was spent as the duty pilot, performing air tests, acting as standby for casevacs or other flying in the vicinity of the capital, and on several occasions, reacting to terrorist incidents close by. During a bush tour with a fireforce, there were very few days indeed when there was no operational flying at all. We were actually on standby around the clock, although normal practice was for one crew to remain on night standby on a rotating basis, whilst the others were allowed to boost the bar profits. It was not uncommon for the fireforce to be scrambled four times a day. In a way, it mattered little if these callouts developed into a punch-up or became 'lemons' where no contact was made with the enemy – the strain on the participants was much the same. Or at least you thought it was until a burst of small arms fire hit your aircraft, your voice went up four octaves and you started making buttons out of the seat cushion covers. The ratio was probably in the order of one in four turning into a contact, but on one memorable day operating with 2 Commando of the RLI in the Birchenough Bridge area, I led the fireforce on three entirely separate contacts where we achieved hundred per cent kill rates on small groups before breakfast. In addition to fireforce duties, the G-Cars were required for casevacs, resupply sorties, deployment of trackers and all the run-of-the-mill tasks, and regularly the whole formation would have to fit in deep penetrations of Mocambique and Zambia to deploy, support and extract SAS or Selous Scout teams.

During this period, some of the force's most experienced pilots were swanning around in South Africa on extended exchange tours flying Mirages. Eventually some of these pilots were brought back to the country for two-week periods to be deployed to the bush – not as aircrew, but as operations officers. A couple of officers flatly refused to go on cross-border operations, and far from facing a court martial, were sent to be instructors, one eventually becoming a squadron commander. I find it incredible to this day that in a war of this intensity, in an air force so small, there was such disparity in the number of combat sorties flown by qualified pilots, ranging from practically zero to several hundred.

It is often unappreciated that the security forces were manned mainly by blacks, and that they were all volunteers. Certainly, they were officered by whites; however, in the latter years of the war, there were to be black officers in all the services, the Selous Scouts having had an extremely brave and highly decorated lieutenant, Edward Piringondo, inevitably long before the decision was made to commission black officers into the other branches.

This lack of entrusting and encouraging the very loyal black population both within and out of the services was a fundamental block in the Rhodesians' thinking. Despite the very obvious success of the only truly integrated unit, the Selous Scouts, there was an underlying feeling that black soldiers were not going to be as aggressive and effective as white troops. Undoubtedly, the all-white Rhodesian Light Infantry on fireforce duties was one of the most effective killing machines seen in modern warfare, but the reluctance to use the Rhodesian African Rifles on either fireforce or, initially, to be parachute trained not only proved to be short-sighted in the extreme, but put an out-of-proportion burden on the young troopies of the RLI. In the same way, there was a reluctance to use mixed sticks, but when the experiment was sanctioned it proved to be an immediate and popular success with both the Rhodesia Regiment and elements of the RLI. As ever with the Rhodesians, it was only tried towards the end of the fighting and thus far too late for the advantages to be beneficial.

Despite a steady influx of qualified people from other militaries, both the army and air force were reluctant to discuss new ideas and tactics, or entertain that their own methods may be wrong or needed modifying or that the enemy was improving his operational abilities. One would have thought that a military starved of the normal intercourse and exchange between allies would have been voracious for new thinking, but the complacency engendered by the early successes never completely wore off, and I have a suspicion that when the first indications of the tightening noose of defeat were felt, the lack of any semblance of a cohesive strategy became apparent and the only response was to ask more and more of the troops who had kept the country alive by engaging in a war of attrition and slaughtering the enemy in his redoubts in neighbouring countries. By that time, it was too late. Had the external camp attacks redolent of the last two years of the war been undertaken in 1975 and 1976, and then a campaign of harassment using random but regular attacks by air been undertaken to prevent the enemy regrouping close to the borders, it could have produced a far different environment for the fledgling multiracial government of Muzorewa and Smith to evolve, before the country was sacrificed on the altar of political expediency by the new Conservative government of Britain in 1979.

The air force make much of the long-range raid to Angola

by the Canberras and Hunters in February 1979. They had been to the limit of their operational endurance and landed back at Victoria Falls with about ten minutes fuel for low-level flying in their tanks. The question that should be posed is why was it not done more often. That's what the crews were trained for, and flying to the absolute limits of your range has been asked of many air forces; speak to a Luftwaffe fighter pilot in the Battle of Britain, a Bomber Command crew of World War II, or an Argentinian pilot of the Falklands campaign. The crews were only too willing; it was the will to utilise them that was required.

I believe this almost paralysis of committing to decisive action was a direct result of the decision to continue to run the air force as a peace-time unit. Promotions chugged along in a predicted fashion, despite the fact that most of the air force command had no knowledge of counterinsurgency warfare in general and helicopter operations in particular. One cannot help wondering how aggressive and effective the air force would have been if Norman Walsh had been leapfrogged to commander in the mid-seventies, with squadron commanders perhaps like Pete Simmonds, Baldi Baldwin, JR Blythe-Wood or Kevin Peinke. Much was made of the 'shooting a dustbin in a clearing' episode, and it is difficult not to sound churlish at what was some good gunnery by Rich Brand, but an air force at war doesn't celebrate party tricks on the range; it looks to the exploits of the gunners, pilots and navigators who are delivering ordnance in a hostile environment.

The task of an air staff is to provide the framework and resources for their operators to perform in combat. The air staff of the Rhodesian Air Force performed abysmally. With a very minimum of exceptions, any officer above the rank of wing commander in 1974 that was still in the force at the end of the war, should as a penance recite the names of the following every day:

Air Sub-Lieutenant	KW	Goddard	KIA	4 Apr 1974	Canberra
Air Sub-Lieutenant	WR	Airey	KIA	4 Apr 1974	Canberra
Flight Lieutenant	BC	Weinmann	KIA	14 Apr 1974	Trojan
Senior Technician	RR	Durett	KIA	14 Apr 1974	Trojan
Air Sub-Lieutenant	RJ	Wilson	KIA	20 Apr 1974	Trojan
Flight Sergeant	RS	Andrews	KIA	20 Apr 1974	Trojan
Air Lieutenant	B	Murdoch	KOAS	17 Dec 1974	Trojan
Officer Cadet	BM	Delport	training	3 Jun 1975	Vampire
Air Sub-Lieutenant	RJ	Boulter	training	19 Jun 1975	Provost
Sergeant (SAAF)	P	van Rensburg	KOAS	23 Dec 1975	Alouette
2nd Lieutenant (SAAF)		Stroebel	KOAS	16 Feb 1976	Cessna 185
Squadron Leader	GA	Routledge	KOAS	16 Feb 1976	Cessna 185
Sergeant	P	Graham	KIA	18 Jul 1976	Alouette
Sergeant	HF	Belstead	KIA	1 Sep 1976	Alouette

Flight Lieutenant	HW	Stevens	KIA	2 Sep 1976	Lynx
Flight Lieutenant	R	Hulley	training	21 Oct 1976	Vampire
Squadron Leader	PA	Barnett	KOAS	6 Jan 1977	Dakota
Flight Lieutenant	DE	Mallett	KOAS	6 Jan 1977	Dakota
Flight Lieutenant	IH	Donaldson	KIA	12 Jan 1977	Canberra
Air Sub-Lieutenant	D	Hawkes	KIA	12 Jan 1977	Canberra
LAC	C	Brown	KOAS	15 Apr 1977	Lynx
SAC	R	Nelson	KIA	17 May 1977	Alouette
Flight Lieutenant	B	Collocott	KIA	31 May 1977	Dakota
Air Lieutenant	DL	du Plessis	KIA	2 Sep 1977	Lynx
Sergeant	JS	Underwood	KIA	2 Sep 1977	Lynx
Flight Lieutenant	P	Haig	KIA	23 Nov 1977	Vampire
Flight Sergeant	A	Fleming	KIA	12 Jan 1978	Alouette
Flight Sergeant	HAJ	Jarvie	KIA	12 Jan 1978	Alouette
Flight Lieutenant	G	du Toit	KIA	28 Jul 1978	Alouette

Sergeant	K	Nelson	KIA	29 Jul 1978	Alouette
Corporal	A	Turner	KOAS	4 Jan 1979	Alouette
Flight Lieutenant	K	Fynn	KOAS	4 Jan 1979	Alouette
Corporal	B	Cutmore	KOAS	4 Jan 1979	Alouette
SAC	A	Wesson	KIA	5 Sep 1979	Bell 205
Flight Lieutenant	PM	Bate	KOAS	27 Sep 1979	Alouette
Sergeant	G	Carter	KOAS	27 Sep 1979	Alouette
Flight Lieutenant	K	Peinke	KIA	2 Oct 1979	Canberra
Captain (SAAF)	JJ	Strydom	KIA	2 Oct 1979	Canberra
Air Lieutenant	BK	Gordon	KIA	2 Oct 1979	Hunter
Flight Lieutenant	AJ	Senekal	KOAS	25 Dec 1979	Alouette

plus 14 members of the Rhodesian Army who were operating as crew members or being carried as combat troops. For it was they who sent these brave men to fight in equipment that, in the years after UDI, they had managed to augment with only a handful of converted civilian light aircraft that they painted green and dared to call light strike aircraft, and very late on some decrepit Huey helicopters that were scrap out of another air force's breakers' yard. They compounded the crime by exhorting them to use the ammunition sparingly, ammunition that would eventually be passed over to the enemy they were fighting, and that many of the same officers would stay on to administrate.

Between 1974 and the end of the war, in one of the most violent and sustained counter-insurgency operations in modern warfare, the Rhodesian Air Force managed to acquire, apart from helicopters, eleven of which were really clapped-out Hueys, some light transport Islanders, some Cessna 337s (Lynx), at best a light observation and FAC aircraft, but which were painted green, lightly armed and used as the primary ground attack weapon, and Sia-Marchetti SF-260s (Genets), which most observers would call trainers, whatever colour you paint them. In fact, after UDI, not a single recognised aerial weapons platform was acquired by the Air Force.

A significant proportion of the Rhodesian population never comprehended that the country was involved in a deadly fight to the death, and the air force staff particularly seemed to operate on the principle that the war was a minor irritation to the business of running an elite flying club. I remember having a conversation with a very senior officer at the time of the Geneva conference, when he informed me that should sanctions be lifted, the first priority for acquisition was 'a new jet trainer'. Which planet was he living on?

I have more than a suspicion that certain elements of the

Rhodesian command structure made an early decision that
the war was lost and were manoeuvring for their positions
in the new state of Zimbabwe long before the end. The book
Pride of Eagles, an otherwise excellent study and subtitled *The
Definitive History of the Rhodesian Air Force*, ends one sentence
short. The missing last sentence should read:

> 'The Rhodesian Air Force then became the first air
> force in the history of warfare to hand itself over as a
> fully functional operational unit to the enemy it had
> been fighting, and then support that enemy in its new
> policy of the ethnic cleansing of a minority group
> within the country.'

But they got their new jet trainers. And a few people even got
to fly them, before they found out what life was really like in
the service of their new paymasters after the sabotage attack at
Thornhill in July 1982.

There have been many recriminations since the
independence of Zimbabwe regarding the betrayal by Britain
of its former colony of Southern Rhodesia, but the question
of betrayal from within has rarely been mooted. This despite
the fact that the commanders of the police, air force, army,
combined operations and central intelligence not only pledged
allegiance to the enemy they had been asking the young men
of the country to combat for so long, but then assisted him to
set about slaughtering the historical Ndebele threat to his own
tribal grouping, and with a complete lack of both moral and
physical courage stood by and did nothing whilst at least one
former member of the security forces, Morrison Nyathi, was
the first of those unlawfully incarcerated, tortured and horribly
put to death by the state they now served.

Afterword

The two G-Cars cross the wide Zambezi and fly for about ten minutes into Zambia. The Lynx overhead acting as Telstar confirms that he has the three men who are to be picked up visual and they have their shirts off, which is the recognition signal that they are not being forced to act under duress and he will direct the helicopters straight in to uplift them. They arrive overhead and one orbits to act as top cover whilst the other lands and uplifts the two black men and one white man. They are filthy and stink as usual and are quite obviously exhausted.

The little formation crosses back over the river and the gunner peers closely at the white guy and speaks over the intercom to his pilot who turns and looks also and then calls to his wingman.

"You'll never guess who we've just picked up. Mike Borlace."

It is true. The day I left Terry Emsley at headquarters during the dirty pistol incident and went for a piri-piri chicken lunch, I'd arranged to meet with Ron Reid-Daly, the boss of the Selous Scouts. I am now a parachute qualified, rotten baboon eating, bearded officer in Rhodesia's special force's unit and commander of their reconnaissance group.

But that is another story.

Appendix

For those few who can actually identify errors or verify my recollections:

"Gentlemen, it was an honour and a privilege to have flown with you."

Those that drew the short straw and had to fly on one or more combat bush tours with me:

Flight Sgt	Alan	Aird	MFC		
Sergeant	Finch	Bellringer			
Sergeant	Beef	Belstead		KIA	1 Sep 1976
Flight Sgt	Rob	Blumeris	DMM		
SAC	Brian	Booth			
Sergeant	Dave	Boyce			
Sergeant	Paul	Braun	MFC		
Sergeant	JB	Britton	MFC		
Sergeant	George	Bushney			
Corporal	Pete	Caborne	MFC		
SAC	Gary	Carter		KOAS	26 Sep 1979
SAC	Alan	Cocking			
SAC	Criv	Crivellari	MFC		
Corporal	Brian	Crystal			
W/O	Geoff	Dartnall	DMM		
SAC	Lionel	Davell			
Sgt (SAAF)		du Preez			
Sgt (SAAF)	Percy	Ferreira			

Flight Sgt	Flammo	Fleming	MFC	KIA	12 Jan 1978
SAC	Mark	Furnell			
Sergeant	Pat	Graham		KIA	18 Jul 1976
Flight Sgt	Butch	Graydon	MFC		
W/O	Johnny	Green	MFC*		
Flight Sgt	Martin	Hulbert			
SAC	Mark	Jackson	MFC		
SAC	JJ	Jacobs	MFC		
Flight Sgt	Henry	Jarvie	MFC	KIA	12 Jan 1978
Flight Sgt	Dave	Jenkins	MFC		
Flight Sgt	Tony	Jordan	MFC		
Sergeant	Burt	Keightly	MFC		
Flight Sgt	Pete	McCabe	DMM, MFC		
Sergeant	Hugh	McCormack	MFC		
Sergeant	Ginger	Morris	MFC		
SAC	Rory	Perhat			
Flight Sgt	Keith	Rayne			
Sergeant	Tweedy	Reid-Daly			
Sergeant	Frank	Robinson	MFC		
Sergeant	Steve	Russell			
SAC	Beaver	Shaw			
Sergeant	Alan	Shields			
Flight Sgt	Doug	Sinclair	MFC		
Master Sgt	Steve	Stead	MFC		
Sergeant	Hansie	Steyn	MFC		
Sergeant	Rob	Thomson	MFC		
Sergeant	Phil	Tubbs	MFC		
Flight Sgt	Mike	Upton	BCR		
SAC	Mario	Venutti			
SAC	Billy	Watt			

And those that got away with only the occasional white-knuckle ride:

W/O	Colin	Bedford	MFC		
Flight Sgt	Finn	Cunningham			
SAC	Brian	Cutmore		KOAS	2 Jul 1979
Sergeant	Carl	de Beer	MFC		
Flight Sgt	Norman	Farrell	DMM, MFC		
SAC		Hicks			
SAC	Chris	Joubert			
Sergeant	Tony	Merber	MFC		
W/O	Chas	Penney			
SAC		Platt			
SAC	Rosie	Rosenberg			
Sergeant	Mike	Rochat			
Sergeant	Phil	Scott	MFC		
Sergeant	Wally	Tolmay	MFC		
Corporal	Tony	Turner		KOAS	4 Jan 1979
SAC	Frank	Tyrell			
SAC	Coenvan	Staden			
Flight Sgt	Wally	Wallace	MFC		
Flight Sgt	Brian	Warren	MFC		
SAC	Alex	Wesson		KIA	5 Sep 1979
Sergeant	Gary	Whittal	SCR		

You will notice, despite scuttlebutt to the contrary, that the only one of you scratched whilst you were babysitting me was Butch – and that was by a coke bottle!

Glossary

A/A	Anti-aircraft
ADEN	30mm calibre cannon fitted to Hunter
AK	Kalashnikov AK47 – semi-automatic 7.62mm enemy weapon
ASAP	As soon as possible
Banjoed	Ambushed
Basha	Temporary shelter
BCR	Military decoration
Bombshell	Scatter (in disarray)
Bonsella	Gift
Braai	Barbeque
Browning	.303 machine gun on helicopter
Casevac	Medical evacuation
Chiloga	Male appendage (slang)
COIN	Counter Insurgency
ComOps	Combined Operations – organisation for directing the war
CT	Communist terrorist
Cyclone	Codename for air force and aircraft
DF/GA	Day Fighter/ Ground Attack
DMM	Military decoration
Donga	Ditch, gully

Doppies	Cartridge cases
Dwang	Trouble
FAF	Forward Airfield
Flot	Front line of own troops – essential for ground attack pilot to know when firing close to own troops
Frantan	Napalm
Freds	Fremilo troops (Mocambique Army)
Flat dog	Crocodile
FRELIMO	Government of Mocambique (Front for the Liberation of Mocambique)
Frozen Area	Area where security force operations were halted as Selous Scouts pseudo team were operating
Fundi	African wise man/expert
GCV	Military decoration
Goffals	Mixed race people
Gooks	Terrorists (slang)
Gridref	Grid reference – unique reference of location on map
GSW	Gunshot wound
H-hour	Exact time of attack
HF	High Frequency – generally for long-range radio contact
KIA	Killed in action
KOAS	Killed on Active Service
Kopje	Hill – generally bare granite on upper levels
Kraal	Group of African huts

JOC	Joint Operational Centre – headquarters for directing and coordinating operations in local area
Lemon	An operation where no contact was made with the enemy.
LZ	Landing zone
MAG	7.62mm belt-fed machine gun
MFC	Military decoration
Madullah	Old man
Main Munna	Senior person
Mictel	Lead connecting radio to headseat
MMWC	(Main Munna What Counts) – chief
Moer-in	Cross with
Neddies	Administrative officers – generally keeping Operations from upsetting the paperwork in Headquarters
OP	Observation position
PATU Stick	Police ANTI-Terrorist Unit ("Black Boots") – unit of police that deployed in the bush for Operations
Phos	Phosphorous
PRAW	Police Reserve Air Wing
QHI	Qualified helicopter instructor
Ratpacks	Ration packs – nominally for twenty-four hour requirements
RAR	Rhodesian African Rifles
Rebro	Rebroadcast radio station
Recce	Reconnaissance
RLI	Rhodesian Light Infantry

Roineck	"Redneck" – derogatory term for newly arrived (hence pale-skinned) Europeans (slang)
RPD	7.62mm terrorist light machine gun
RPG	Rocket-Propelled Grenade ("Bazooka") – Armour-piercing weapon, shoulder-launched. Highly dangerous to helicopters
RR	Rhodesia Regiment – infantry unit
RT	Radio Transmission
RV	Rendezvous
RWS	Rhodesian Women's Service
SAM-7	Shoulder-launched, heat-seeking guided missile
SAS	C Squadron Special Air Service
SB	Special Branch
SCR	Military decoration
SF	Security Forces
Sapper	Engineer
Shebeen	Beer drink
Sigint	Intelligence derived from intercepting radio traffic
Sitrep	Situation Report – formal appreciation of situation
SKS	7.62mm terrorist carbine
Slope	South African (slang)
SMG	Sub machine gun – generally 9mm calibre
Sneb strike	SNEB rockets – air-to-ground weapons. Two calibres – 68mm fired generally from Hunter, and 37mm fired from light ground attack aircraft

Snottie	Snotnose – as after a punch on the nose (slang)
SOP	Standard Operational Procedure
Stick	Smallest Rhodesian fighting force – generally consisting of four men to be compatible for helicopter lift and consisting of three riflemen and an MAG gunner
Strella	SAM-7
Subbies	Junior officers
Telstar	Radio relay
Terrs	Terrorists
TF	Territorial Force soldier (call-up soldier)
ToT	Time on target
Troopie	Generic term for soldiers
UDI	Unilateral Declaration of Independence
Veldskoens	Bush shoes (desert boots)
VHF	Very High Frequency – generally for short-range radio contact
Vlei	Open area in the bush
ZANLA	Enemy troops under control of Mugabe and based in Mocambique (Zimbabwe African National Liberation Army)
ZIPRA	Enemy troops under control of Nkomo and based in Zambia (Zimbabwe People's Revolutionary Army)